"Carrie . . . You Know I Want You,"

Nikolai said, his voice husky.

Me and how many other women, Carrie thought.

"But there is so little time—I want to get to know you better, to take you out to dinner, to buy you presents, to tell you how beautiful you are."

"Is that what you usually do?" Carrie couldn't stop herself from asking.

"It's what I want to do," he said simply, disconcerting her with the sincerity of his words. "But since time is so short," he went on, "I'll have to speed things up . . ."

"How?" Even as she spoke, he reached for her hand, pulling her onto his lap.

SERENA GALT

is a resident of Worcester, England, and *Double Game* marks her debut as a Silhouette author. She works full time and writes when she can. Serena enjoys romances and tries to re-create in her work the mixture of passion and tenderness that is characteristic of the genre.

Dear Reader:

SILHOUETTE DESIRE is an exciting new line of contemporary romances from Silhouette Books. During the past year, many Silhouette readers have written in telling us what other types of stories they'd like to read from Silhouette, and we've kept these comments and suggestions in mind in developing SILHOUETTE DESIRE.

DESIREs feature all of the elements you like to see in a romance, plus a more sensual, provocative story. So if you want to experience all the excitement, passion and joy of falling in love, then SIL-HOUETTE DESIRE is for you.

Karen Solem
Editor-in-Chief
Silhouette Books

SERENA GALT
Double Game

Silhouette Desire

Published by Silhouette Books New York

America's Publisher of Contemporary Romance

SILHOUETTE BOOKS, a Division of Simon & Schuster, Inc.
1230 Avenue of the Americas, New York, N.Y. 10020

Copyright © 1984 by Serena Galt
Cover artwork copyright © 1984 Herb Tauss

Distributed by Pocket Books

ISBN: 0-671-49859-2

First Silhouette Books printing July, 1984

10 9 8 7 6 5 4 3 2 1

America's Publisher of Contemporary Romance

Printed in the U.S.A.

BC91

1

Two remarkable things happened to Carrie the afternoon of her first-round match in the Italian Open tennis tournament. The first was that she defeated the number two seed, Mireille Villefour; the second was that halfway through the match she realized a man was watching her.

There was nothing very unusual in that, perhaps. Hundreds, thousands of people paid good money to watch top tennis players. Even on a minor court tucked away near the kitchens, pervaded by a smell of olive oil and tomatoes—even at midafternoon, when most Italians would still be eating or sleeping—the stands were more than half full of spectators.

But this man was different. He sat in the front row of the box reserved for players, but he wasn't a player. He was too old—mid fifties—and massively fat, and he stared at Carrie uninterruptedly from the moment she stepped out onto the court until the umpire called the last point, when the crowd, filled with sentimental Italians, rose to applaud the victory of the young, pretty newcomer Carrie over the thirtyish, tough professional Mireille. And his scrutiny was neither the interest of a tennis fan nor the male admiration inspired by watching a very attractive young woman in a very short tennis dress. He watched her deliberately, as if he were judging her; even when she rested in between games he watched her, and from time to time she found herself meeting his expressionless gaze.

The last point played, Carrie ran to the net, received a muscular handshake and a grim "Well done" from the disappointed Frenchwoman and stood for a moment savoring her victory. It was amazing, unbelievable; she had never before played so well. All her hard work and her father's coaching was paying off at last.

But in her joy she was conscious of an undercurrent of apprehension—the fat man was still watching her—and then she had no time to think at all, for the press were let on to the court.

In America, where Carrie had been playing since January, photographers and reporters were carefully controlled. Officials protected the players from them, and the whole proceeding was professional and well-managed. But now it was Perugia in May, and the Italian press were surging and rushing and babbling and jostling round Carrie and Mireille. "*Per favore!* Smile, smile, lady! What does it feel like to win?" Most of them were calling out in Italian and Carrie, was momentarily bewildered. An indifferent Mireille walked away, ruthlessly thrusting the photographers aside, leaving Carrie to her fate.

"Foreigners!" said Tony Astell, Carrie's father and

6

coach, standing beside her protectively. He was delighted at her win; grinning all over his reddened freckled face, he gathered up her spare rackets and hustled her into a quiet little anteroom.

"I've got news for you. Splendid news!" He paused, waiting for her to ask what it was. Carrie, suddenly exhausted from her three-set match in the punishing heat, longing only for a shower, looked at his eager face and could not disappoint him.

"What is it?" she asked, dropping into a low leather chair and wearily unlacing her shoes.

"Karel Vronsky wants to speak to you." As Carrie had never heard of Karel Vronsky, the dramatic effect of her father's declaration was lost. "Nikolai Zanov's coach," he pursued, undeterred. Now Carrie did know what he was talking about. Nikolai Zanov was one of the best male tennis players in the world—an exuberant, talented, handsome, gifted, impossible Russian. Carrie had seen him often enough—playing his superlative tennis or picking a verbal fight with a hapless umpire, urged on by his legions of female fans—and in the newspapers, pictured at nightclubs or with some beauty queen or model. He seemed to go out of his way to seek publicity, and she was torn between admiration for his tennis and exasperation at his behavior.

"Is Karel Vronsky a fat man in his fifties?" she asked. "Because if so, he watched me all through the match."

Tony Astell was shocked. "You mean you noticed him watching you? Where was your concentration, girl? I've told you and told you, when you're on court, you keep all your concentration *inside* the court—never mind what's happening anywhere else."

"What does he want?" Carrie was still disturbed by

7

Karel Vronsky's scrutiny. "What have I to do with Nikolai Zanov?"

"A great deal, in the next month," her father said, gloating. "They want you as his doubles partner."

"But he always plays with that Rumanian girl."

"She's injured."

"Which tournaments does he want me for?"

"The French championships, and Wimbledon."

Carrie laughed, relieved. "Oh, that's ridiculous. I'm not nearly good enough. Say no for me," she said, and made off toward the showers.

But in the passage the fat man barred her way.

"Please, a moment; let me congratulate you on a splendid win." His English was heavily accented but correct. Carrie could see now that his intent expression was not so much menacing as anxious. "It is important that you listen to me. There are no other women of your quality free for mixed doubles," he went on. "Nikolai wants you as his partner."

"Wants me? He doesn't even know me," said Carrie, confused.

"He saw you last year. In Florida. He wants you."

"And what Nikolai Zanov wants, he gets, I suppose," said Carrie, determined not to be one of the many women who fell over themselves for the slightest word from Zanov.

"Do consider it," said her father. "Think, Carrie. This could be the chance of a lifetime."

Carrie thought of the hours her father had devoted to coaching her and made up her mind. "I won't say no, but I won't say yes till I've talked to Zanov myself. Will that be possible?"

"Oh, yes," said the fat man, letting out a breath of relief. "We are at present in Rome for ten days. When you are finished here, I suppose you go to Rome?"

So it was arranged, and Carrie went to take her shower, puzzled and intrigued to know that she interested Zanov so much that he had sent his coach all the way to Perugia to ask her in person. And about mixed doubles—never an important game to a player of his quality.

Several days later Carrie was honorably defeated in the semifinal of the singles by the American champion. Her disappointment was tempered by delight at having gotten so far. For the past five months she'd practiced or played a match on every single day not occupied with traveling. Now even Tony Astell—who didn't allow family sentiment to affect his ruthless coaching—felt she deserved a rest.

So at seven o'clock on the evening of her semifinal defeat a bouncing, glowing Carrie tossed her last suitcase into her little hired Fiat and prepared to set out for Rome. She stood for a moment gazing at the city round her, a medieval city, red stone glowing in the evening sun, the stepped roofs stretching away beneath her to the Umbrian plain. The narrow cobbled street echoed with footsteps and the sound of the wooden wheels of a cart piled high with melons. Behind her a church clock struck seven.

"You look mighty cheerful, considering Martina just mopped you up in two straight sets," observed Dallas Parfitt, the lively young American who partnered Carrie in the women's doubles. "Where are you off to?"

"Rome," said Carrie.

"Tonight?"

"Why wait? If I stay here, people will only talk to me about tennis. At the moment that's the last thing I want."

9

"Tony going with you?"

"No, he's coming down tomorrow."

"Where are you going to practice?" demanded Dallas. "I'll be in Rome soon, and we can work out together."

"Not likely. I'm taking three days off."

"No tennis?"

"No tennis," said Carrie happily. "No tennis at all."

"So what'll you do?" Dallas was aghast at the prospect of going so long without tennis. She'd played every day since her sixth birthday.

"Shop. Look round Rome; it's one of my favorite cities. Meet people. Enjoy myself."

"Whatever you say." Dallas stepped back as Carrie started the engine and sped away through the narrow streets.

With an exhilarating sense of freedom Carrie pointed the little car in the direction of Rome. Fond as she was of tennis, it wasn't her whole life, as it was her father's and her younger brother Jimmy's. If Jimmy, an established professional player at twenty-one, hadn't damaged his knee so badly that he was out of the game for two seasons, Carrie's life would have been very different. At twenty-two, art college behind her, she'd been just beginning to establish herself in the creative-design department of a London advertising agency. Until she'd moved to London, she'd always helped her parents with their tennis coaching school near Brighton and had distinguished herself as a junior player, but being an Astell, she could hardly have done otherwise. Tony Astell, for so many years the best English amateur player, had married Betty James, Australia's Wimbledon champion for two years running, so how could a daughter of theirs be other than proficient at the game?

Since she could walk Tony had encouraged her to practice, to develop her shots, to train, but Carrie had had other ideas. In her spare moments she drew and painted and looked at paintings till she had trained her eye as far as she could and till the sweet, vague art teacher at her private school could teach her no more. Her father had no patience with art as a subject and held that since the camera had been invented it was a waste of time painting; but he was devoted to his daughter, and if painting was the career she wanted, he would indulge her.

He was actually proud of her when she distinguished herself at art school and then secured a prestigious and well-paid job; but when Jimmy, the tennis hope of the family, was injured, Carrie felt she had an obligation to join the family business. The tennis school needed publicity; in a recession people were less interested in paying for lessons. Her father, whose commitment to British tennis was total, relied on his paying customers to subsidize the free help the school gave to promising young players. He needed a player of real quality to coach and accompany round the world circuits. When Tony came to stay at her flat in London and began leaving entry forms for minor American tournaments all over the place—her roommate Louise even found one in the bread box—Carrie decided she'd return to tennis for a year or two. "Just till Jimmy's recovered," she said firmly. "As soon as he steps on court again to play a match, I retire."

There was no sign of that day coming, at least this season and Tony appreciated his daughter's steadiness and determination, working at something she only half enjoyed. But then she had her mother's temperament —independent, courageous, loyal—and was far more consistent than the impulsive, quick-tempered men of the family. And she also possessed, as Tony was discovering to his delight, her mother's marvelous talent for tennis. Tony had no illusions about the limits of his own gift; at his best he had aptitude for the game, which he had developed to its utmost by hard work and concentration. Jimmy was very much the same. But Carrie . . . Recently he'd begun to hope she might be a champion, like her mother, with a magic combination of steady nerves and flair.

As Carrie stamped on the accelerator of the little Fiat and drove along the highway, she felt anything but steady. She felt like a horse let loose after being cooped up in the stable too long. She wanted to kick up her heels and run. In the last two seasons she'd earned substantial sums of prize money. Much had gone for expenses, but there was still a good deal left, and she had wads of Italian lire—hard-earned—in her bag. Tomorrow she would go and buy clothes. *Not* tennis clothes, she thought, nothing useful—feminine, flirty clothes, to go out to dinner in.

She would have one occasion to dress for, at least. Ben Jackson, Jimmy's friend and doubles partner and Carrie's escort for the past year, was in Rome preparing for the Open. He would certainly ask her out, Carrie knew, though she didn't look forward to it. She seldom analyzed her own feelings for Ben, but lately she'd become aware that soon she would have to decide whether to accept him as a lover or to stop seeing him altogether.

And then she remembered Nikolai Zanov, that disturbing man. Perhaps he would ask her out too, and he certainly would show her none of the consideration and gentleness she was used to from Ben. Zanov's reputation had gone before him—a ruthless user, then discarder, of women. Had she caught his attention as a tennis player or as a woman? She couldn't see that her tennis was sufficiently outstanding to warrant such trouble—but she also couldn't see that he would find her all that attractive. His usual companions were totally different from the more athletic Carrie; they were creatures of the limelight: models, actresses, rich socialites. Perhaps he'd like a tennis player just for a change, she thought, and lifted her chin in rebellion. He may take other women for granted, but he's getting nowhere with me, she told herself.

It was late when she reached her hotel after twice getting lost in the outskirts of Rome. She collapsed gratefully into the room Tony had booked for her, noticing only that it was narrow and high-ceilinged, with windows at each end.

The next morning she woke bathed in sunlight, trying to identify an insistent noise. Car horns! Parp parp, parp parp, they sounded like bumper cars at an amusement park. She hung out of the front window and caught a glimpse of the stream of cars clogging the Via Veneto row upon row, all making an unholy din. At least they're Roman cars, she said to herself, and wandering to the back window, pushed aside the shutters. Beneath her was a little courtyard no larger than a room; a profusion of plants and vines covered the low stone wall that surrounded the central fountain; and a slender nymph modeled in bronze now green with age held aloft a conch shell. Water from the shell played delicately on the surface of the pool, and Carrie was spellbound by the beauty and peace of the scene.

Downstairs the expansive holiday feeling of being suspended in time was rudely broken. There were three notes for her at the desk: Ben Jackson would pick her up for dinner at eight that evening; Karel Vronsky had arranged a meeting with Zanov for that afternoon, so could Carrie come to the stadium where he was playing, please; and a reporter from *Paris-Match* had left a telephone number, would Carrie ring him to arrange an interview, please.

Carrie, delighted with her new clothes and turning many Italian heads, took her seat in the stadium to watch the end of Nikolai Zanov's exhibition match just after the time Karel Vronsky had set. At first she thought it was over. The crowd was screaming and stamping, and no play was in progress. Then she realized that the Roman crowd was living up to its reputation for partisan hooliganism. Judging from the scoreboard, Zanov was leading his Italian opponent two sets to one, five games to two, and the crowd didn't like it. Soft drink cans and small coins showered the court at Zanov's end, and the umpire, vainly appealing for order, made no headway while the tall Russian waited, his long tanned legs caked with red clay dust, his heavy dark hair clinging damply to his neck. Arrogant and spoiled he might be—but he stood on court looking every inch the magnificent athlete and magnetic male animal, his broad shoulders tapering to narrow hips accentuated by close-fitting shorts. His attitude of contemptuous indifference was enraging the crowd still further, and Carrie wondered how long it would be before he was goaded into one of his notorious tantrums.

At last, when it was clear the crowd would not settle down, Zanov took his rackets and towels from the umpire's chair after a brief exchange with the umpire and strolled to the exit with insolent self-possession. A young man leaped onto the court and barred his way, snarling insults. The top of his head barely reached Zanov's chest, and the Russian kept walking with the youth swinging on his arm.

Carrie was impressed despite herself by his nonchalant strength and the brooding force of his presence. Her wish to interview him and reject him as a possible partner suddenly seemed over-confident. The man who cared so little for an enraged Italian crowd would surely dismiss a mere woman with contempt if she didn't fit in with his plans. She hurried to the players' section to meet him.

Vronsky was nowhere to be seen, and none of the Italian officials was expecting her, so she positioned herself near the door he would emerge from. Several Italian girls were waiting there too, tennis groupies waiting for their favorite hero to emerge. Carrie wondered idly how many of them were Zanov's fans.

Ten minutes later she had the answer to her question when he emerged from the doorway, protected by solid-looking men in trenchcoats; all the female fans swarmed round him, and caught by surprise, she hurried after him as fast as she could in her fragile Italian shoes. "Mr. Zanov!" she called, dismayed. "Mr. Zanov!"

He leaped into a waiting Ferrari and started the engine. Carrie, only one of the swarming crowd of female fans, abandoned hope of attracting his attention. He stared indifferently ahead, waiting for his bodyguards to clear the way for his departure. Two press photographers were recording the scene; Zanov's gaze rested on them, calculating; then he seemed to come to a decision. His eyes swept along the row of imploring faces, and his dark, compelling gaze met Carrie's indignant blue stare.

Imperiously he pointed her out to one of his bodyguards. Grim-faced, humorless, the man came over to Carrie and urged her roughly into the car. Before she realized what had happened, she was sitting beside Zanov and his arm was around her, posing for the photographers. Pressed against his body, she felt hers thrill to his touch; the warmth of his grip and the imperious charm of his expression as he looked down at her for the picture almost overwhelmed her. Then he looked away and the car surged forward. They were off, out of the stadium.

He drove in silence. He was dressed in casual clothes—dark, close-fitting trousers and a white shirt open to reveal the dark tan of his muscled chest. His hair was still spiky and damp from his shower, and his athletic body asserted itself arrogantly in the confines of the car. Involuntarily Carrie shifted away from him. She could still feel the tingling in her shoulders from where his arm had touched her so casually. He seemed to feel nothing of the electricity she'd felt when their bodies touched—or had he? Certainly he was watching her now with a puzzled expression in his dark eyes as she struggled to compose herself.

Nervously she brushed a strand of golden hair from her cheek and tugged the skirt down over her knees. He draped his arm round her, his long fingers resting lightly on the curve of her breast. Carrie was indignant. She resented his cavalier treatment of her, and at the same time she was unable to deny the involuntary response his strong fingers evoked in her.

"Can we get down to business, please?" she said coldly, shrugging his arm away.

He glanced at her in astonishment. "You're English!"

"Of course." Carrie was enraged. He didn't know the least thing about her. His obvious amusement didn't help.

"I've never met quite such a businesslike fan," he said. His voice was deep and beautiful—but too arrogant, thought Carrie, catching herself up. She mustn't let his obvious attractions confuse her.

"I'm not a f—" she began, but he stopped the car, and before she knew what was happening, she was in his arms, his lean body pressed tightly against her, his curving mouth insistently, demandingly, on hers. For a moment her senses leaped in soaring response, and her body moulded itself to his. Then, as his fingers slid down to her breast, she jerked away. "How dare you!" she spluttered, her rage fueled by the desire of her treacherous body. "Why are you treating me like this?"

He started the car abruptly. "What did you expect?" he demanded. "You're a very desirable woman. You hang around waiting for me to notice you—then you get in the car with me. What did you think I was going to do, give you a guided tour of Rome?"

Finally, Carrie realized the obvious—he thought she was a groupie. Either Vronsky hadn't told him about the appointment he'd arranged, or Zanov had forgotten. Relieved by this simple explanation for his rather unconventional behavior, she smiled.

He noticed her smile, his face alert, and commented, "You are strong—for a woman." She remembered only how weak her body had felt in his viselike grip.

"That's from playing tennis," she said. "It keeps you fit, don't you find?"

"Tennis? What do you mean?" he asked with a quick frown.

"I mean that I'm Caroline Astell. Karel Vronsky asked me to meet you and discuss being your doubles partner."

Zanov tapped his face with the palm of his hand in an extravagant gesture of surprise and apology. "Ah! I forgot! But you do not look like Carrie Astell. She wears her hair in a ponytail."

"Not always," Carrie returned. "I only wear it that way to keep the hair off my neck when I'm on court."

His mobile face expressed bewilderment, almost regret. "Believe me, Carrie, I am sorry. It was a mistake. I thought you were—"

"Never mind that," interrupted Carrie, anxious to avoid the subject of his kisses.

"Was it such an unpleasant experience?" His dark, thickly lashed eyes mocked her with an intimate knowledge of her response.

"This is strictly business," said Carrie.

"So you say. Well, what have we to discuss? Will you play tennis with me, or won't you?"

Carrie saw they were approaching her hotel. Relieved at the prospect of escape, she asked him to stop the car. "I'm not sure about the partnership. . . . I'll let you know," she said, realizing she was being feeble but unable to control her racing thoughts. He caught her hand and, pulling away, she was once again conscious of the power of this man. "Talk to Karel about the details," he said, and drove away, apparently convinced that she'd agreed.

Carrie looked after the retreating car in a welter of conflicting emotions. She was mortified that he hadn't even recognized her—that showed how little she mattered to him—and she was too bewildered, too overwhelmed by his dominating personality, too confused by her own unprecedented response to him, to think clearly. She brushed her lips with her fingers. Originally she'd hesitated to involve herself with Zanov because of his unpredictability. Now added to that was the fear of where the involvement might lead. Nikolai Zanov was not a man to be trifled with. She didn't want to be just one in a long line of his conquests, and she didn't want to be hurt. And yet instinct told her that a relationship with the Russian, though it might be hectic and dangerous, would certainly also be exciting. Perhaps too exciting for Carrie's peace of mind.

Now was the time to find Karel Vronsky and explain that she couldn't agree to play tennis with Zanov. But she didn't.

Carrie's dinner with Ben Jackson that evening should have been idyllic. They sat in a romantic garden overlooking the Colosseum; Ben was tanned, and it suited him, thought Carrie, looking at him objectively. Most women would find him appealing enough—tall, well-built, with even features and thick, springy auburn hair. But he kindled no spark in her, and she avoided all his attempts to turn the conversation toward his feelings for her.

She fell silent and sipped her wine, entranced by the view over the city and trying to keep her thoughts away from Nikolai Zanov.

"I hear you've had marvelous luck," said Ben, reading her mind. "Playing with Nikolai Zanov, no less."

"It isn't decided yet," said Carrie, guiltily remembering that her father was even now back at the hotel preparing a special analysis of mixed-doubles tactics for her to work on.

"Surely you wouldn't turn him down? It's an amazing opportunity."

Carrie, half-listening, savored her wine and reflected. Tony and Ben were right, of course. As far as publicity and making a name for herself were concerned, she had no choice. But those considerations hardly interested her. They were important only as far as her father was concerned. In one more year Carrie would be out of tennis and back to advertising.

She still didn't understand why, according to Vronsky, Zanov was so determined to have her as his partner—why he bothered to find a partner at all. For a player of his stature the mixed doubles event was an entertainment, a self-indulgence almost. Perhaps she should ask Zanov to explain his motives.

Even now as she sat with Ben she could imagine Zanov's eyes burning intensely into hers; half-unconsciously she rested her fingertips on the place his hand had held her arm. I don't like arrogant men, she told herself; I don't like playboys. "Arrange it with Karel" indeed! She hadn't agreed to be his partner and—suddenly decisive—she made up her mind she wouldn't. And she would let him know that night. As soon as dinner was over she would leave a note at his hotel, and then she could forget him.

This settled, she felt much better and could enjoy Ben's undemanding company. He'd just arrived from England and was telling her all the Brighton gossip and plenty of news of her mother, who apparently was extremely pleased about Carrie's success in the Italian Open. "She always said you'd turn out a better player than Jimmy. So did I, of course, but then I'm prejudiced." He chatted on about tennis and his chances in the men's Italian Open and tried to get Carrie to agree to lunch with him the next day if she couldn't manage dinner. Carrie meanwhile was mentally composing her letter to Nikolai Zanov.

"You're not listening to me," he said finally. "It's not like you to be so vague, Carrie. Are you ill? You don't look it. You look beautiful."

"Thank you," said Carrie, becoming more and more aware that she must get away and settle matters with Zanov once and for all.

2

~oooooooooo~

The Russians' hotel, stately, dignified, expensive, in a prime position on the Via Veneto, was only a few hundred yards from the Astells'. Carrie was determined to deliver her note in person before seeing her father could influence her decision again. She said her good-byes to Ben and stood for a moment hesitating outside the ornate revolving doors. The man at the reception desk was most helpful. "Mr. Zanov? Of course, signorina." He snapped his fingers, and Carrie found herself following a bellboy up the shallow carpeted stairs and along the baroque corridor of the first floor. "I only wanted to leave a note," she said to the bellboy, but he sped along ahead of her.

"*Per favore, per favore.*" He hustled her into a small plush hallway and abruptly retreated.

Eleven o'clock. Funny time to bring me up here, she thought. Perhaps he's giving a party. Two doors led from the hall. Behind one she heard music, a

Brahms symphony she recognized. It was too late for second thoughts, she realized. They wouldn't have let her past the reception desk if he'd wanted to be left undisturbed—and it wasn't a bad idea to disturb him for once instead of letting him get away with disturbing the rest of the world.

There was no answer to her knock. She knocked again and pushed the door open. The room was filled with sound. It was a long room, heavy with luxury and gilt decoration, festooned with velvet curtains and carved furniture with marble tops. The music was everywhere, hundreds of instruments reproduced on a massive hi-fi system. It flooded every corner, every carved crevice, with Brahms.

Nikolai Zanov did not look round as she came in. He lay stretched out on a gilded sofa, back to the door, utterly still and listening with fierce intensity. She shut the door quietly. She knew the symphony was nearly over, and she didn't want to disturb him. He was so completely relaxed, every limb heavy like a wild animal in repose. She too was captured by the beauty of the soaring strings.

The last notes sounded, and there was silence, the loudest silence Carrie had ever heard. Slowly he rose to turn off the hi-fi, and he saw her. Only a momentary pause betrayed his surprise; then he smiled a warm, welcoming smile, as if they were old friends.

"How long have you been here?"

"Five minutes. Maybe more."

"Standing by the door all that time?"

"I didn't want to interrupt. The music—there was so much of it, all around, like a living thing."

"Are you a musician?"

"Not in the least, I just like listening. Especially to Brahms."

"Sit down and we'll listen to more. What would you like? Another symphony? The violin concerto—?"

"No," interrupted Carrie. "I only came to drop a note at the desk, but they misunderstood and brought me to see you instead."

"And what does the note say?"

She held it out to him. He read it, then crumpled it in his hand. "So we will not play together," he said, head on one side, regarding her quizzically. "Not even tennis?"

"Not even tennis," said Carrie. "You'll find someone else."

"Already the Russian tennis authorities have a partner in mind for me. Not so pretty as you, nor so good at tennis, but a good Party member."

"That's all right then," said Carrie, puzzled. There was an undercurrent of meaning in his voice that she didn't understand.

"I am not just a tennis player, you see. A famous Russian abroad is, in the eyes of the Soviet authorities, a performing poodle who must do the right tricks at the right time. The Party would prefer a good Communist close to me. A tennis partner would be ideal," he said. "But that's not your problem. Tell me one thing. Why did you come to see me this afternoon?"

"To say I couldn't work with you because you shout and throw tantrums on court. It's not my style. Not that I wasn't flattered to be asked."

Zanov sat down and pointed to a chair. "You must explain. What is your style?"

"Peaceful and straightforward. I'm not good enough to cope with distractions."

"But aren't you interested in the publicity you'd get?"

"No; my father is, of course—he coaches and

manages me—but I'm not looking for a career in tennis," Carrie explained, and when she had finished, he laughed.

"We are in the same boat, then," he said. "I too do not want to hit a ball over a net all my life. But in my country the government decides what you will do, and if you have talent, there you are. Your life is planned for you and made very comfortable and easy; all is organized and provided, and you are a person of importance in the Soviet Union. I need to be important."

Once again she sensed she didn't understand the reasons behind his words. "What did you want to be, if not a tennis player?"

"Ah, I won't tell you. You will laugh."

"Why should I?"

"But you will." He seemed amused himself. "You must promise not even to smile; then I will tell you."

"I won't promise, just try me."

"I wanted to play the violin."

"In an orchestra, or solo?"

"Whatever I was good enough to do. I still play, of course, but"—he shrugged—"you know as well as I do, keeping fit for tennis is a full-time, if stupid, occupation."

"I don't think it's funny at all," said Carrie with spirit. "Why should it be? Being a musician makes as much sense as running round hitting a tennis ball. Actually I think it makes more sense. But then I would, wanting to be an artist myself." She thought a moment. "Couldn't you just stop playing tennis and become an ordinary citizen?"

"My country is different from yours. Politics is very important there. Disagreeing with what the authorities say is a serious problem. I have a sister, Sonya, who is what you in the West call a dissident. So she gets into trouble, again and again. While I am a famous sportsman, a hero of the Soviet Union, while I am known abroad and the Western press will print what I say, I can help Sonya, protect her a little."

"Couldn't you do that as a violinist?"

With a wave of his hand he dismissed the idea. "Violinists are two a penny in Russia; they grow on trees. Tennis players, no."

"That's terrible," said Carrie slowly, feeling for him. "You mean your whole career has been spent on something you don't even like?"

He dismissed that, too. "No, no, I like tennis well enough as a game, but not as my whole life. Even in a year or two or three, when I am no longer so successful and they let me retire and coach the team, I will have to try and spin out my playing career if I am to be any help to Sonya."

Carrie considered the problem. "And Sonya won't change her opinions?"

"They are her opinions," he said simply.

"You could always let her take full responsibility for them."

"Oh, I could; that is what she says, over and over again. She almost hates me for insisting that I do what I can for her. But think, Carrie. If you had a little sister, how would you feel if she went to a labor camp, perhaps to die? You are playing tennis to please your father, not to save his life. How much more would you do if it were a matter of life and death?"

Carrie could say nothing. This Zanov was very different from the man she had met that afternoon, the man the public knew. There was none of the haste, the offensive arrogance, only the intimacy of shared understanding.

Carrie was very aware of the fact that they were alone together. Zanov knew from her response to his kisses that afternoon that she found him attractive. She was acutely aware of him as a man, of the short distance between them, of his dark eyes appreciating her and of her own longing for his touch . . . and yet she hardly knew him. How was it possible to feel so much, so soon?

With a deliberate effort she concentrated on something else. "Why did you want me as your doubles partner in the first place? I understand why you wouldn't want the Communist girl spying on you, but why me?"

Nikolai laughed. His face changed from its habitual expression of cool indifference to lively amusement. Even his eyes, usually measuring and detached, were alight with laughter. "So you are not perfect after all!" he said. "You are human enough to fish for compliments. What shall I tell you—that you will be a champion tennis player? That I desire you? What do you want to hear?"

Disconcerted, Carrie realized that she did want appreciation from him, which was unusual, but then her whole response to Nikolai was uncharacteristic. "I'd rather you told me the truth," she said, not knowing whether he was serious.

"That was the truth," he said, "but not the reason I wanted you for my partner. Those seem . . . futile now."

"Why?"

"Let me explain. I saw you play in Florida last year. Against Navratilova."

"I remember. She beat me six-one six-one in the first round. It was a pity. I was playing well."

"You were indeed. That's why I stayed to watch.

You had your hair in pigtails, and you looked about fifteen, running round the court, fighting every point and smiling even as you lost."

"It's hard not to admire Navratilova. She's such a great player."

"That's all very well in theory, but most players wouldn't take that attitude while being beaten all round the court. I thought then that you must be one of the few women in top tennis who were still playing the game of tennis—as opposed to a business. You were enjoying it."

"And you wanted to play with someone who enjoyed the game?"

"Yes. Someone genuine, unspoiled. Someone different."

"I'm sorry that it hasn't worked out," said Carrie, getting up. Zanov stood up also.

"Let's meet tomorrow," he suggested. "Let me show you Rome."

"I'm not sure . . ." said Carrie. "I'm not going to change my mind about our partnership, you know." She could imagine nothing better than to see Rome with Nikolai, but she also knew that already she cared too much what he thought, what he said, what he felt. His dark eyes fastened on her.

"It doesn't matter," he insisted. "I want to see you anyway."

"Have a good time with Ben?" said Tony, hardly looking up from his notes and diagrams as Carrie joined him at the breakfast table. "The coffee's cold, I think. Better order some more. I must have a word with Zanov about tactics. He always plays at the net, I remember, but that was with the Rumanian. She can't volley. You've got a good net game, my girl, and we should exploit it."

He looked up and noticed her appearance. "Lord, you're all dressed up! Where are you off to?"

"I'm only wearing an ordinary summer dress." This belittling reference to an exquisitely cut Italian confection of embroidered cream silk ought to convince her father, Carrie thought; he was utterly indifferent to fashion. He himself chose to wear trousers cut so generously that in a wind they flapped like sails around his legs. But she was not to get away with this so easily.

"I've bought dresses like that for your mother in my time," said Tony dryly, "and the prices were anything but ordinary. Don't tell me you're going out with Ben?"

"No," said Carrie, reluctant to mention her companion for the day. She didn't want any analysis or discussion about Zanov. Above all she didn't want to explain to her father why she was spending the day with a man she wasn't prepared to play tennis with. After all, Tony would argue, it was only two tournaments. Just the French Open and the Wimbledon championships.

Carrie didn't understand her own motives, so how could she explain them? She knew that the thought of spending the day with Nikolai Zanov made her heart beat faster, made the sun brighter and the breakfast more delicious.

"You don't have to tell me who you're going out with," Tony said in high good humor. "I know, it's your holiday. Going sketching?"

"Sight-seeing," said Carrie as the waiter brought fresh coffee and a bowl of grapes arranged with true Italian care. "Rome is a wonderful place. Everywhere you look it's like a feast for the eyes. Vegetable stalls, butchers' shops—"

"Ruddy awful stadium they play the Open tournament in—"

"I'm just talking about what it looks like," said Carrie patiently. "Those grapes, for instance." Tony stared blankly at them, and she abandoned her attempt to explain the principles of graceful arrangement to him.

Feeling guilty at preventing him from the pleasure of meeting Zanov that day, she hovered in the front hall until the dark blue Ferrari drew up outside, when she ran down the steps and got in beside him. He looked very handsome but remote, his expression hidden behind dark glasses.

"Where are we going?" she asked, her high spirits rather dashed by his aloofness.

"Everywhere," he said, with a sudden, charming smile. "Today we will do everything tourist, nothing sophisticated. We will see the best, the most obvious, sights, the clichéd places that are clichés because all sensible people want to see them. I've even brought a camera." He gestured toward the glove compartment, and she looked inside, impressed by the expensive equipment and dismayed by his withdrawal behind a man-of-the-world facade.

"What is worrying you?" Always quick to pounce on any change of mood, he noticed her hesitation. She avoided the hand he stretched out to her, unable to explain the depth of the impact he had on her and her reluctance to commit herself physically in any way before she knew what he felt for her. "Is there another man; is that it?"

"No other man," said Carrie firmly.

"Then why do you draw away from me?"

"I . . . don't know you well enough yet," she said.

"You don't know me well enough to hold my hand?" he teased, and Carrie blushed, assailed by warmer memories of what had happened between them and what she wanted to happen.

But from then on he was very careful not to touch her, avoiding even the most casual brush of the fingers on her arm, not even helping her in and out of the car. Yet she was acutely aware of him. His sport shirt and faded jeans covered but could not hide the muscular grace of his body, a constant magnet for her eyes. Now and then he caught her watching him. He made no comment, but the amused look in his eyes told her that he knew the effect he had on her. Arrogant, she thought; conceited, vain.

Apart from this, he was an ideal guide to Rome. He knew when to talk or to be silent, and he loved Rome. There was so much to see that only particular moments impressed themselves on Carrie—standing on the Via Sacra in the Forum, whose paving-stones had been laid perhaps at the very foundation of the city, while half-wild cats, unawed by history, leaped from ruined arch to fallen column and lizards basked in the spring sun, half-hidden in the weeds. She would later remember the silence in the gardens of the Vestal Virgins as a light breeze stirred the water in the long pool, then the distant voices, the rustling of pines and the rich scent of spring flowers.

Lunch was a happy affair in a chance-found restaurant in a back street near the Spanish Steps. They ate *tagliatelle* in ham sauce, drank Frascati wine, looked back in triumph on the success of their morning and made plans for the afternoon. One hour stretched into two as they drank coffee and learned more about each other.

"Tell me how you learned such good English," said Carrie finally, realizing she'd forgotten it wasn't his native language. His deep, clear voice held only a hint of foreignness, and not in accent but intonation.

"I am almost English; my grandmother came from Sussex."

"That's where I live!"

"I know, you told me. Don't interrupt." His teasing expression belied the abrupt words. "It is a romantic story, so you will like it."

"I'm not especially romantic," denied Carrie.

"All women are. Do you want to hear the story, or don't you?"

"I do, I do." Carrie subsided.

"When my grandmother was seventeen, she came to Russia to stay with cousins; that was before the revolution. She fell in love with a passionately committed revolutionary, and her cousins, from an aristocratic family, threw her out. She married her young man and stayed in Russia with him, through the bad times—and for her they were very bad. She had five children; only the youngest, my father, survived childhood, and he died in a labor camp before reaching thirty. My mother was also dead by then, so my grandmother took care of Sonya and me. I've always spoken English and Russian; neither one is my mother tongue, and I know more about the countryside of Sussex than I do about any of Russia except Moscow."

"Were they all bad times? Wasn't she happy with your grandfather?"

"When he was there, very happy, but he was in and out of labor camps, each time older, more worn, hoping for a little less and fearing a little more."

"But she still loved him?"

"Oh, yes, she still loved him."

"Then I expect she made the right decision, don't you?"

He shook his head emphatically. "Certainly not. I would never expect to marry a woman from the West and ask her to settle in Russia. The cultures are too different." With a deliberate movement of his hand he dismissed the subject. "Choose how we spend the rest of the afternoon," he said.

Carrie, happily listing the places she wanted to go, trailed away into silence. He was no longer listening; he was staring over her shoulder. She turned and saw Karel Vronsky approaching. Pleased, she greeted him, but he ignored her and spoke in urgent Russian. Nikolai replied, and they argued back and forth; with a sinking heart Carrie realized that the idyll was over; the reality of Nikolai's restricted and supervised life had returned.

Finally he turned to her. "Carrie, I must go. I am sorry. Karel will take you back to your hotel."

"I can find my own way back," said Carrie, trying to sound neither martyred nor offended, and knowing that she would prefer to be alone. But Zanov insisted, and the drive back to the hotel in Vronsky's car was tense with unasked questions. The fat man did not even attempt small talk, and Carrie was grateful. As she got out he said, "Zanov wants me to tell you he will meet you at your hotel at eight o'clock tomorrow."

Prompted by his grim expression, Carrie stated, "But you don't approve, do you?"

"It is not my business to approve what he does or who he meets," said Vronsky bitterly. "I am only the coach. I don't make decisions; I don't say what I think." Carrie doubted that. He seemed the kind of man who said what he thought most of the time, and it would probably be sensible.

"You asked me to be Zanov's partner," she pointed out. "What do you have against him seeing me? Why did you follow us today?"

"Who says I followed you?"

"You must have. We found the restaurant by accident; if you hadn't followed us there, you couldn't have found it."

The fat man jerked his head in a dismissive gesture. "Don't try and think, stick to playing tennis; work on your service, it's still not fast enough; and change those shoes." He indicated her high heels. "You'll turn your ankle and you'll be out for the rest of the season."

"But why did Nikolai have to go just now? And where did he go to?"

"Mind your own business."

"Tell him I'll be ready tomorrow at eight," said Carrie, unoffended. Vronsky wasn't aggressive but preoccupied and nervous.

The remainder of that day and the whole of the next was uneasy for Carrie. She couldn't settle down. With all of Rome to see and to sketch, nothing caught her attention. She wandered through buildings of breathtaking beauty just to occupy her time. The weather itself was in sympathy with her moods. Heavy gray skies and drizzling rain changed to bursts of sun that touched the orange-red buildings into triumphant life; in the same way Carrie at first felt cast down with the knowledge that Nikolai was having difficulties of his own and was reluctant to become involved with her, then exultant with joy that ran like a river through her blood. Every word he had said to her, every touch, was remembered. She had never been so intrigued by a man; her body had never responded so fully before. The sensible part of Carrie knew that Nikolai was the sort of man women felt like that about; she knew she had small reason to suppose he returned her feelings. Perhaps he lavished the same attentions on every girl who attracted him. But she still looked forward to seeing him that night.

Just about noon, she realized a man was following her. And he wasn't following her the way an Italian bent on an amorous encounter would, but pursuing her with a relentless deliberation, with no attempt to keep out of sight. He was thirtyish, a clean-shaven man, good-looking in a pallid, blond style, stocky and dressed in an American lightweight suit. At first she thought he was a tourist too. It was hardly a coincidence that he should be at the Vatican when she was and then at the Trevi fountain, though she noticed he didn't throw in the mandatory coin—but that he should also be interested in women's shoe shops and sporting equipment stores seemed too much of a coincidence altogether.

Her instinct was to confront him, but as she walked in his direction he stood his ground, ignoring her, and something in the coldness of his light blue eyes choked Carrie's words before they were uttered. He had an American haircut, short and brushed; he should have been attractive, but the chilliness of his expression and demeanor made him eerie.

A shaken Carrie returned to the hotel and made arrangements to practice that afternoon with Dallas Parfitt; no longer wanting to escape from tennis, she welcomed the reassurance of doing something so thoroughly familiar and physically taxing. The company of the American girl was also welcome; supremely incurious where anything other than tennis was concerned, Dallas perfunctorily inquired whether Carrie had enjoyed her holiday and then without listening for a reply threw herself with relief into what she thought of as real life.

Carrie realized with a shiver of unwelcome perception how many people's lives were led without any awareness of others. Her father was preoccupied with his children's success; Zanov was thinking of his sister; Dallas had all of reality narrowed down to a rectangle of ground marked off with lines and divided by a net; and the Frozen Man, the blond who had followed her—what, she wondered, was his reality? And had she gotten in his way?

After the game, her muscles pleasantly tired from the exercise, Carrie showered and dressed with great care. She wanted to look sophisticated so Nikolai would be impressed, cool so that he would be tantalized, beautiful to arouse his desire. When she was ready, the reflection that looked back at her from the mirror was only half-familiar. Her golden hair was twisted up on top of her head, and she'd made up her eyes carefully. Excitement lent color to her cheeks, so she only needed to add a touch of lipstick. Pretty, healthy, cheerful Carrie was gone; in her place an exquisite, elegant woman.

Slightly dazed from the success of her efforts, Carrie stepped into the hotel foyer, ready to leave, only to find three photographers waiting with her father.

"What's all this?" she said lightly, expecting a celebrity until she saw from the expression on her father's face that the photographers were there at his request; once again he was doing his best to publicize his daughter and advance her career. She was about to burst into angry speech, but he forestalled her. "A good time to tell the press about the new partnership," he said.

"What new partnership? I'm not going to play with Zanov. I never told you I was. Anyway, just playing mixed doubles for two tournaments isn't news," she said, irritated.

"It is if Zanov's involved. Especially if there's a romantic involvement."

"A romantic involvement?" Carrie was baffled. Her father would never have noticed her state of mind; he was supremely unobservant about emotional matters. Then she realized he was winking at her.

"They're not to know he's not in love with you, are they?" he whispered.

More angry than she could say, Carrie turned to the photographers. "Please go away," she said. "There's no news here."

With the consideration to be expected of paparazzi, they started to encircle her and snap pictures.

"What the hell is this?" Zanov stormed into the foyer. "A press conference, I suppose. With me as chief character."

"I thought the world should know about you and Carrie here," said Tony with unfortunate emphasis. Carrie cringed inside but met Zanov's eyes coolly as her father went on. "It'll be the greatest partnership in mixed doubles," he continued, and she couldn't listen as Zanov's gaze turned from questioning to contemptuous. She couldn't tell the Russian she had nothing to do with the scene—not while her father was there. She worried that Nikolai was so angry that he might say or do something to annoy Tony Astell, and though Carrie was furious with her father, she knew he was doing what he thought best for her career and the cause of British tennis. She also knew his great admiration for the Russian.

So she tried to put a good face on it and took Nikolai's hand for the photographers and tried not to feel him pulling away from her. She thought the flashbulbs and questions would never end, but at last they were driving away in silence.

Carrie cleared her throat. "Nikolai, let me explain."

His expression was blank behind dark glasses. He said nothing. His body was almost menacing, it was so still, so tense, under the tailored cloth of the tuxedo.

"Do take those glasses off. I want to see your face. My father must have misunderstood my decision about our partnership. And I had nothing to do with those photographers, honestly."

"*Honestly,*" he mimicked her savagely. "Honestly you had nothing to do with them. That is why you didn't send them away. That is why we stood there grinning and nodding and you have thousands of dollars worth of free publicity at the expense of good old Nikolai, who was naive enough to believe he'd found a woman who didn't want to misuse her power over men: a woman interested in someone other than herself."

"You're wrong," said Carrie, "if you think I invited the photographers . . ."

He stopped the car abruptly in a tiny square, deserted except for an old man sitting on a stone bench in front of a blank and shuttered church. "Then why did you play up to them? Why didn't you send them away?"

"You don't understand—" she began, but he interrupted her savagely.

"I understand more than you think. I've been through all this before—"

"Been through all *what*?" Carrie was furious at his arrogant refusal to listen to her. "If you won't let me explain, I'll get out of the car now."

"And walk back to the Via Veneto in that dress and those shoes? What kind of attention do you think you'd attract?" His mocking gaze seemed to pierce right through her flimsy clothes, making her feel naked and vulnerable. Gazing out of the window, struggling to regain her composure, she noticed a dark Peugeot had parked close to them. With a thrill of horror she recognized the Frozen Man sitting calmly in the driver's seat, watching her.

"Nikolai, look at that man," she said urgently, their argument forgotten. "I saw him this morning—"

Nikolai clicked his tongue derisively. "I knew you wouldn't walk back to the hotel," he said, and Carrie lost her temper.

"You're impossible. Why won't you listen to me? And why would it matter so much if I did want publicity? It's not a crime."

"Are you going or staying?" he asked with insulting indifference.

She got out and slammed the car door. "Have a pleasant evening," he said, and drove away.

The sound of his engine died in the cool air, and the square was silent. Stunned, Carrie started to walk back to the hotel.

It took her half an hour, and her feet hurt acutely toward the end, and always—ten yards or so behind her—crawled the dark Peugeot.

3

The next morning in the reassuringly normal sunny hotel dining room, Carrie felt her fears fade into irritation with Nikolai's arrogant behavior. All around her Italian families and tourists were drinking coffee, eating rolls, planning their day's activities; the man in the dark Peugeot seemed almost a figment of her imagination. Certainly he was not the threat he had been the night before.

Tony Astell joined her. "Enjoy yourself last night?"

Carrie shrugged and sipped her coffee.

"Tell me what Zanov made all that fuss about. Is he publicity-shy all of a sudden?"

"I don't know exactly," said Carrie. "The real trouble was I'd told him I wouldn't play with him and that I wasn't interested in publicity."

"And are you still determined not to play with him?" Tony's expression was anxious, apologetic. He wanted this partnership so much. Carrie realized her refusal seemed whimsical to him. She couldn't explain her instinctive shrinking from further contact with Zanov—nor his attraction for her.

"No," she said, "but I don't know how he'll feel about it since last night."

"I'm sorry if I made things difficult for you, Carrie. You know I wouldn't want that." His freckled face was earnest; she patted his hand affectionately. In the light of the bright dining room, the little fountain splashing reassuringly away in the courtyard outside, the dark world of intrigue seemed far away indeed. The shadowy fear that had haunted her the night before—of the man in the dark car that had crawled so threateningly through the streets of a Rome grown suddenly hostile—returned for a moment, and she shuddered with a chill despite the warmth.

"You're upset about something," said her father.

"I think Nikolai has problems of his own that I can't even guess at," she explained.

"These Iron Curtain athletes often do," said Tony. "I don't want you disturbed in any way, Carrie. Are you sure you want to go ahead with this doubles partnership?" That he even asked the question was a measure of his concern for her as a person, not just as a tennis player, and Carrie appreciated it.

"I'm sure I want to go on with it," she said, her decision the result of much tossing and turning the previous night. She didn't understand her own feelings completely, but she knew she was already involved with this passionate, turbulent, unpredictable man, too involved to let him disappear from her life so easily.

Tony was obviously relieved at her decision and went to make arrangements for their flight back to England that afternoon. Once she'd packed, Carrie wrote a brief impersonal note to Nikolai telling him of her decision and delivered it to the reception desk of his hotel.

As she moved, cuts and bruises on her feet were painful reminders of her walk the previous night; when she sat down to look at the Italian newspapers, it was only to see herself and Nikolai staring up at her from the sports pages.

The painful hours dragged by, and at last the taxi came to take them to the airport, but there was still no word from the Russian. With mixed feelings of regret and relief, Carrie watched Rome dwindle away to a toy city as the airplane rose, circled and set course for England.

In England Carrie quickly settled down to a routine that was both physically tiring and blissfully uncomplicated. She was training at home so that Tony could coach her and supervise the tennis school at the same time. It was a joy to be in England again after touring for more than six months, and the Sussex countryside was glorious with spring blossom.

Her brother Jimmy was looking well, and the reports about his knee from his doctor and physiotherapist were good, but he seemed irritated by the idea of Carrie playing doubles with Nikolai Zanov, and he criticized Zanov on several occasions. One evening Carrie was sitting by the window in the huge kitchen-living room that was the heart of the house. Her mother, Betty Astell, used it for entertaining on all but the most formal occasions, so that she wouldn't feel she was missing anything while preparing the food. The kitchen of the four-hundred-year-old farmhouse was a long room, with original oak beams in the low ceiling and the original heavy wood kitchen table, big enough to seat over twenty people; the stone flags on the floor were shiny and uneven, worn by generations of feet. The scent of roses drifted in through the diamond-paned casements, and Carrie was dreaming, drowsy with tiredness, when Jimmy sat down beside her.

"I don't trust that man," he said. He looked like a younger version of Tony Astell, with a narrow freckled face and a thin, wiry build. His sandy hair was cut short and bristled from his head as if it crackled with the energy of his combative personality.

"Who?" said Carrie, blinking back to awareness. "Don't shout at me, Jimmy."

"I wanted to wake you. I'm talking about Zanov. He's got a terrible reputation, you know."

"So you're going to give me a brotherly warning?" said Carrie, half-amused, half-annoyed at Jimmy's presumption.

"He never stays with one woman long."

"You're an authority on his private life, I suppose," said Carrie dryly.

"He's got the most public sex life on the men's circuit, and that's saying something."

"I don't believe all I hear," said Carrie, "and I suggest you don't either. I also suggest you remember that we're only playing tennis together."

"You've got to admit it's odd, Carrie. Why would Zanov want you for a partner? Not just for your tennis, that's for sure."

"Let's leave it. I'm too tired to argue, and it's none of your business, younger brother." She spoke lightly but even tactless Jimmy knew better than to pursue the subject once she had dismissed it.

She sat on alone by the window, and the real problem touched on by his words loomed large in her mind. Nikolai Zanov was already very important to her—but how important was she to him? He hadn't written, hadn't even sent a message to say he was glad they would be partners for the French Open. Perhaps it didn't matter to him. There was no way of telling.

The next day Tony Astell agreed to let Jimmy give up his coaching at the school. It was something Jimmy hated and was unsuited to, being far too impatient and inarticulate to teach anyone anything; he left for Rome to cover the men's Italian Open tournament for a Fleet Street newspaper. Carrie was not sorry to see him go, and the Astell household lapsed into peace.

It was strange to be back in England, within easy reach of London yet utterly out of the advertising world she had thought of as her life. When she had returned to tennis, she had given up her flat in Notting Hill Gate and packed up all her possessions. Most were now in boxes in the attics of the Sussex house, but hanging in the wardrobes of her room were all her London clothes, two years out of date now, with the few additions from Rome hanging forlornly as a reminder of the intense emotions she'd felt when wearing them. Otherwise she lived in track suits, tennis dresses and training shoes. She thought of calling up her London friends, but then decided against it. She had no time to spare for seeing them, anyway; her waking hours were all occupied following her father's training schedules.

Once she was watching television, too tired to go to bed, when an advertisement she had designed was shown. It was effective, more effective even than she had hoped, and she felt a pang of regret for her lost

job and way of life. It would be difficult to get back into
advertising unless she was exceptionally lucky. It took
years to establish yourself, and she hadn't had those
years.

But her regrets were few compared with her pleasure in the tennis school's success. The courts were
occupied throughout the day, and her parents were
kept busy coaching.

After a year back in the game Carrie knew that she
was at last approaching peak fitness; her weak shots
were now strong, her strong shots winners, and her
service was as powerful as any in the game. All the
time she practiced—running, swimming, spending
hours on the court practicing again and again, sending
the ball into the marks Tony made for her within an
inch of accuracy—she thought with amusement that
Nikolai Zanov might be surprised in his partner. She
knew too much about tennis, had lived with it for too
long, to have any false modesty about her play. She
knew the next two months, especially the French
championships and Wimbledon, might see her transi-
tion from a promising newcomer to an established
champion. Even in her most optimistic moments she
didn't expect to win the Wimbledon singles—not this
year. But she no longer missed her work. One morning she realized that she hadn't pined for the office or
for her drawing board for weeks. She hadn't even had
an idea for a design. Perhaps she was more of an Astell
than she thought. She was gripped by the pure
satisfaction of doing something difficult and doing it
well.

Her father was delighted with her, and the British
press seemed to share his optimism. Hardly a day
passed without Carrie glimpsing reporters and pho-

tographers in earnest consultation with her father. For two afternoon practices she was surrounded by photographers, but Tony didn't allow her training to be interrupted for interviews.

One morning very early she was jogging on a cliff path that followed the curving line of the coast, with the blue Sussex sea rolling and breaking on the rocks far beneath her. She was doing interval training, jogging and sprinting alternately, and as the path neared the road she began a sprint, uphill and into the wind. A car was parked on the road, a large anonymous car; she registered out of the corner of her eye that it belonged to no one she knew, and she knew most of the residents in that small village.

"Carrie? Carrie?" The voice, a voice she could never mistake for any other, drifted toward her on the wind. She stopped to catch her breath, and Zanov moved toward her, strange in his formal dark clothes. He was dressed for town in a dark suit and overcoat, and his eyes looked haggard, as if he'd been driving all night. In a moment, without thinking, she was in his arms, and he hugged her fiercely, protectively, as if he would never let her go; he could feel the strength of his body against her, trembling with emotion.

At last, shaken, she looked up at him. "What in the world are you doing here?"

"Seeing you," he said, his dark eyes teasing, his long fingers brushing the fair hair from her damp forehead.

"The last time we met you weren't so . . . friendly."

"I must apologize for that. I had a long talk with your brother in Rome, and I put two and two together. Those photographers were your father's idea—right?" She nodded and brushed aside his apologies. Being in

46

his arms felt as natural as breathing. It was as if in the days she hadn't seen him their relationship had advanced—as if she knew him better. With a little sigh she relaxed against him. His first tight embrace loosened, and his hands gently started to stroke her back. His eyes were fixed on her face, full of tenderness and a kind of hunger. "You're so beautiful," he said, and she responded to his tenderness by clinging to him, holding him closely.

She could feel his fingers on the heated skin of her back move lazily, caressingly. Her whole body seemed focused on the pleasure; the ripples of excitement his touch had aroused in her from their very first meeting were intensified by the feeling of intimacy and trust between them now. Overwhelmed by the feeling of his arms around her, his body against hers, Carrie slid her hands down his tautly muscled torso. Nikolai looked down at her, his dark hair whipped by the breezes, and started to kiss her, placing tingling cool kisses on her neck and face. She was entranced by his confident power as his mouth covered hers, nibbling her lower lip, tantalizing her, then withdrawing. His lips were firm, and the morning roughness of his unshaven face rasped challengingly on her soft cheek as she clung to him, her lips opening under his probing tongue, suddenly weak.

The noise of a passing car brought her back to reality, and she stepped away from him and saw him clearly. He was pale, tired, his face drawn with weariness and perhaps, she guessed, anxiety. She could feel the chill of early morning. "Come and sit in the car," she said, and he opened the door for her, installed himself and started the engine so he could run the heater. He was shivering.

"Are you injured?"

"No. I wanted to see you, so I withdrew from the tournament and drove from Rome."

Carrie's heart leapt with joy at this. "How long are you here for?"

"As long as I can stay. Sooner or later Karel and the others will find me. My time is not my own. In ten days we have to go to Paris, in any case."

For a moment they sat in silence, seagulls wheeling and screeching overhead in wild lament, the distant sound of the sea murmuring and breaking on the rocks in its eternal advance and retreat. Carrie was very conscious of the strength and warmth of his hand. Gently he lifted her chin, and his lips met hers in a kiss holding tenderness and longing but no passion; he was deliberately keeping himself aloof.

Carrie was baffled by his lack of explanation. He had come from Rome to see her, but why? Why didn't he explain?

"Are you going to stay with us?" she asked, hoping to find out more of his motives.

"Thank you, but no. I've already booked at a hotel in Brighton."

"You can talk to my mother about that," said Carrie, confident that Betty Astell wouldn't take no for an answer. She loved guests, especially tennis guests. "I'm not going to run anymore this morning," she said. "There's only a mile to do, and I'll fit it in later. Drive me home and we'll have breakfast."

The Astell house stood a little back from the road, a long, low, typical Sussex building in timber and warm rose brick. In front of the house the flower beds and lawns slumbered in tranquillity, but the tennis courts behind were buzzing with activity. Tony Astell was coaching four keen local boys, twelve- and thirteen-year-olds who showed promise and were prepared to put in the hard work required before and after school. Carrie explained this to Zanov as they walked up the stone-flagged path.

"Does the state pay fees for this coaching?" asked Zanov politely.

"No one pays. The boys can't afford to—and the government wouldn't dream of it."

"So your father gives his time free?"

"Yes. It's what he believes in, you see—the revival of British tennis. He thinks we have as much talent as any country in the world; we just lack the resources. That's what most of the money Jimmy and I make goes into—Tony's fund," explained Carrie, pushing open the front door. "Come on into the kitchen and meet my mother."

"Won't she be asleep?"

"Not a chance. This is when she does the cooking."

The house was filled with the smell of fresh-baked bread: as they entered the kitchen Betty Astell was busy moving the racks of loaves and buns from the cooker to the table.

With only a brief explanation from Carrie, her mother took over and sat Zanov down at the table; then she started preparing breakfast, chatting easily to him about the Italian Open. Carrie went to shower and change, conscious of Nikolai's scrutiny of her curves under her damp and clinging running gear, and wanting to freshen up.

When she returned to the kitchen it was to find Nikolai sipping coffee and talking tennis to four awed teenage boys while Betty prepared what promised to be a giant's breakfast. With an admiring glance at Carrie's legs in her brief white tennis shorts, Nikolai answered the boys' questions and promised to watch them practice the next day, if their coach had no objection.

Tony arrived in his usual whirlwind of activity, blinked a little in surprise at the unexpected visitor, then set himself to making plans. "You don't have Karel Vronsky with you? No? I'll help your training all I can, of course." His eyes were gleaming with enthusiasm. He had longed for the opportunity to work on Zanov's half-volley, which he was convinced was all wrong.

"I'm resting my leg at the moment," said Nikolai, "but could you spare the time to help me plan tactics for the French championships?"

"Delighted," said Tony briefly.

"Off to school with you," said Betty to the teenage boys who were hanging round the kitchen staring at Nikolai as if they would learn something about tennis from the way he drank coffee. "Mr. Zanov will still be here tomorrow, and he's hungry. How can he eat if you watch him like an animal in the zoo?" And when they still protested, she pushed them out, jokingly but firmly. "Nikolai and I have come to an agreement, Carrie," she went on. "He won't stay in the house, but I told him I wouldn't hear of a hotel. So we compromised, and he'll stay in the flat over the stables."

"Right," said Carrie, and after Nikolai had finished eating she took him over to the flat. It was about fifty yards from the house, above one-time stables now used as garages; secluded and self-contained, the flat was often used for visiting coaches or players when the main house was full.

Carrie led the way up the wooden staircase and into the flat. As her voice explained the practical details she was very aware that they were alone together. "This is the living room, the kitchen—" she pushed open the door to show him—"and this is the bedroom."

He walked in and she followed. It was a charming room with sloping ceilings, gabled windows and flower-sprigged wallpaper, but with Nikolai standing there it seemed small and feminine. His shoulders, broad under the cloth of his city suit, blocked out the light from the windows, and his relaxed but alert stance reminded her of when he stood on court at Rome facing a hostile crowd with apparent indifference.

"You can park your car in one of the garages," said Carrie, talking for the sake of it, enjoying the feeling of his eyes on her. His gaze made her feel desirable and conscious of her body, and she waited for him to make a move toward her. Instead he turned and opened the window, then looked out at the green grass and clay tennis courts, the flower beds and orderliness of the English garden. She went and stood beside him. "What are you looking at?"

"Have you lived here all your life?" he asked.

"Until I was eighteen. Aren't I lucky?" Her attention was only half on the conversation; the rest of her was aware that her head barely reached his shoulder, that she was waiting for him to touch her.

"Very lucky. Carrie . . ." he said, his voice husky, and turning toward her tilted her face up to his. "You know I want you."

Even as Carrie nodded she thought, Me and how many other women?

"But there is so little time."

"How do you mean?"

Impatiently he turned away from her, removed his

jacket and threw it on a chair. "Time to get to know you, take you out to dinner, buy you presents, tell you how beautiful you are."

"Is that what you usually do?" Carrie couldn't stop herself from saying.

"It's what I want to do," he said simply, disconcerting her by the evident sincerity of his words. "It's the least you deserve."

"A proper courtship," said Carrie lightly, still uncertain, afraid to be serious.

"But as time is so short," he went on, "I shall have to speed things up a little."

"How?" said Carrie, eyeing him warily. He sat down nonchalantly in a large chintz-covered armchair, yawned, stretched his linked arms over his head and watched her, amused. She could feel the electric response he kindled in her, even though they were feet apart. "I'll go and get on with my training," she said with an assumption of indifference, but without moving.

"Don't go," said Nikolai. "Watching you is giving me great pleasure. Ever since that night in Rome, I've been imagining this. Being with you. Talking to you. Touching you." As he spoke he reached for her hand and pulled her toward him, onto his lap. At first she struggled, startled, but his arms imprisoned her and she leaned against his chest and savored the rough masculine smell of him and the firm grip of his hands.

She was used to being decisive, having her own way, knowing what she wanted. This feeling of submission and of delicious anticipation was new to her. Nikolai was such a strange blend of arrogant assurance and tender consideration. She watched his face, so close to hers, assertively handsome with its high cheekbones and piercing eyes. She could feel the rhythm of his heartbeat.

Gently he started stroking her neck, and she closed her eyes and abandoned herself to the sensation, delicately arousing and reassuring at the same time. Gradually she felt the sensations spread through her body as his hands moved from her neck to her bare arms, and she watched his fingers, dark tan against the lighter honey brown of her skin. Just as the sensation seemed too intense to bear he started stroking her legs; his fingers closed round her ankle, brushed lightly up the inside of her calves, her thighs. She shivered and, no longer able to accept his caresses passively, unbuttoned his shirt and pressed her lips to his chest. She could feel the roughness of his hair, the smoothness of skin over muscle, and the involuntary shudder he gave as her lips touched him.

"Carrie, Carrie, I want you," he said, his voice hoarse with desire. She looked up and his mouth descended on hers. It wasn't like the delicately probing kiss of earlier that morning; now he was demanding and she responding at a much more immediate, urgent level.

The cool air touching her breasts briefly brought Carrie to her senses, back from the maelstrom of emotion. Nikolai had slid off her shirt and bra with swift, fluid movements and then he stopped and simply looked at her, his pleasure evident in the expression in his darkly lashed eyes. She had no doubt of the effect she was having on him; she could feel his aroused masculinity, and her own nipples hardened in response. His hand moved to cup her breast, savoring its firm fullness, and she arched toward him, longing to be closer, longing for the feeling of his mouth on her. As if reading her thoughts, he bent his head and traced a delicate, thrilling path down her collarbone around the curve of her breast, encircling her nipple with his tongue.

Carrie was lost in the sensation of the moment, hardly aware of his teeth and lips teasing her and the rhythm of his hands on the delicate skin of her inner thighs. Utterly abandoned to him, she was lifted in his powerful grip and laid on the bed.

He gazed down at her, enraptured by the picture she made, her skin satin smooth and warmly honey tinted against the rougher texture of the cream coverlet, her golden hair a radiant mass in the rays of the morning sun. "You are so beautiful," he said, removing his shirt and tossing it onto the chair. Carrie reached her arms up to his muscular torso, longing to feel the hardness of his body on hers, but he remained aloof, his fingers busy at the waistband of her shorts. She lifted her hips to help him slide them down and away, and then she was naked except for a tiny pair of lacy briefs.

He lay beside her and her hands moved across his chest, his back, the muscles stirring under her touch. He pulled her on top of him and held her, his long fingers memorizing the curve of her shoulder, the line of her back. She kissed him deeply and searchingly. Eager to feel his naked body against hers, she slipped one hand inside the waistband of his trousers, and his groan of response encouraged her to explore further. The intimate touch was incredibly exciting, and Nikolai's response was immediate.

Soon he was naked and moving demandingly over her, one hand sliding up her inner thighs till she parted them with a yielding sigh and he was touching the very core of her, tantalizing and pleasuring at once.

"Please . . . please," Carrie said, her legs curving around his back and pulling him to her, then into her until they were moving in a closeness that gave and promised still more ecstasy. "Please," she gasped again, unendurably excited by his strength, clinging to him, gripping him to her. She was abandoned to him, giving herself completely, longing for the final release.

His need matched hers, and their bodies moved together in an ever-quickening rhythm. In the surge of her passion Carrie felt even more acutely the longing to give, to be taken by this man, to belong to him. She could feel him holding back, waiting for her, and this tenderness plunged her over the precipice, her whole body shuddering with sensation till he abandoned restraint and yielded to her.

Minutes later they were still clinging together, the mingled sweat drying on their cooling bodies in the ocean-scented breeze. Carrie was happy, happier than she had imagined possible. She felt utterly at one with Nikolai, as if they had sealed a pact. She waited confidently for words of affection, for promises for the future. She met his eyes openly, not attempting to disguise her love, but he turned his head and rolled away from her. She scrambled under the covers, shaken.

"Don't look like that," said Nikolai brusquely.

"Like what?" said Carrie, shocked. The change in his manner was too cruel. Was it that having had her, he no longer wanted her?

"So . . . eager," he said. "So trusting. So loving."

"Why shouldn't I be?" she asked lightly, but hoped for a serious answer.

"You know I can't promise you anything," said Nikolai harshly. "You know I have no future with you."

The words hung in the air; they stung Carrie like a whiplash. *No future with you.* So final. And to say them now, when they had just shared such an emotional experience—at least it had been emotional for her. But apparently for him it had just been physical. Carrie huddled the bedclothes round her, miserable, and watched Nikolai dress.

"Why are you getting up?" she said finally, not wanting to be hurt further but longing for an explanation. "What went wrong?" She heard herself sounding like a disappointed child.

"I shouldn't have done that," said Nikolai.

"*You* didn't do it," said Carrie, stung. "*We* did it, and I don't regret it at all."

He sat down beside her, buttoning his shirt. "I think I'd better not stay here. It'll be impossible to be so close to you without trying to make love to you. I want you so much, Carrie." He touched her cheek with infinite tenderness. "You are so—so true, so kind."

"I sound like a welfare worker," said Carrie, trying to strike a less solemn note. She was bewildered; a man of Nikolai's sophistication and experience surely knew better than to behave like this. She could only assume that he was genuinely deeply concerned for her and that his concern was making him awkward, even cruel.

"Perhaps I should go," he said again. "Back to Rome."

Was he waiting for her to press him to stay, or was he simply thinking aloud? It was impossible to tell. "You're welcome to stay as far as I'm concerned," said Carrie, pretending to a calm and control she certainly didn't feel. She longed for his company, for his touch, for his lovemaking, but now was obviously not the time to say so.

He gripped her hand and smiled. "Kind Carrie," he said absently, his mind evidently on other things.

"Stop saying that," snapped Carrie. "I'm not kind. I *want* you to stay."

"Well then I will," he said. "I'll get my suitcases." And a very confused Carrie was left alone, the deep emotions of only a few minutes earlier still very much with her.

4

For the next few days matters between them remained in this unsatisfactory state. Carrie, pride hurt,
kept herself a little aloof, careful not to touch Nikolai
accidentally, even when a casual gesture of his to help
her on with a sweater or to pass her a tennis racket
would naturally have resulted in physical contact. She
found it intensely frustrating. Often she longed to run
her fingers through his unruly dark hair or slip her
hand inside his shirt to stroke the muscles of his chest
and shoulders. In her dreams he held her close and
their bodies moved together, but in the daytime it was
very different, all tennis and formality.

He ran with her in the early morning, helped her
with exercise equipment, watched her practice; in
between times he and Tony held several conferences
about tactics for the mixed doubles matches to be
played in Paris. Zanov and her father got on very well

together, Carrie was surprised to see; she'd thought the Russian's arrogance would be an obstacle, but in fact he seemed to be a great success with the Astell parents. He also helped to coach Tony's early morning teenagers.

Watching him with the boys one morning, Carrie was impressed by his wholeheartedness; he cajoled and shouted, teased the boys and persuaded them to improve with as much energy as if a major championship were at stake. After he finished with the boys, he joined her in the kitchen. "Come out with me this evening," he said. "There's a concert at the Festival Hall I want to hear—Brahms."

Before she could answer Betty Astell joined them and the concert outing was being discussed as a fait accompli. Carrie didn't object; she would at least enjoy the music, she knew, and she longed to be alone with Nikolai again.

Carrie was satisfied with her appearance when she went to tell her mother she was leaving. She'd chosen her dress with great care—ostensibly simple, it was a black cotton dress that revealed the smoothness of her shoulders and arms and hinted at the curves of her slender, firm body.

"You look lovely," said her mother, taking in every detail of her appearance. "You've had a special sort of glow recently."

"Oh?" said Carrie, looking away. Her mother was uncomfortably perceptive sometimes.

"Is that the dress you bought in Rome?"

"One of them." And then, thinking to distract her mother from Nikolai and her feelings for him, Carrie added, "Ben admired it."

"Ah," said her mother thoughtfully. "And that was important to you, I suppose?"

"Don't you like Ben?"

"He's very anxious to please," she replied noncommittally.

"Unlike Nikolai."

"Ah," said her mother again. "Now there's a very interesting man."

"Don't you like him either?"

"How could I not like him? How could any woman not like him? He's an attractive man. But dangerous. And unhappy, don't you think?"

Dangerous? wondered Carrie. Her mother was not given to exaggerating; she was a practical, down-to-earth person. "What on earth do you mean?"

Betty Astell looked at her daughter thoughtfully. "Perhaps I'm wrong. I hope so. At any rate he's a marvelous tennis player." Then, briskly, "Don't forget your shawl, my girl, it'll turn cold later."

For the first few miles Nikolai drove in silence. His well-cut tuxedo made him look sophisticated and civilized, but there was always a hint of incongruity when he was formally dressed, always a hint of wildness, of ruthlessness beneath his suave exterior. She watched his long, strong hands resting lightly on the wheel and remembered the sensations they had evoked in her. And why, she asked herself again, had he spoken no more to her about his feelings, his reasons for coming to see her in Sussex? Not just for a one-night stand evidently. Oh, well, she thought. He'd talk to her when he thought it was time; there wasn't much she could do to hurry him without nagging.

She gazed at the passing countryside and remembered something he had told her. "Your grandmother's family came from Sussex, didn't they? Do you know where exactly? Do you have any relatives still living?"

He shook his head. "There's no one left. Her family used to have a manor house near Crowborough, but it was pulled down after the last war and now there is a housing estate in its place. My grandmother was very pleased when she heard that, because now over a hundred families can live where one had lived before. She was very idealistic, my grandmother."

Carrie could guess from his affectionate tone the depth of his feelings for the old woman, and she asked more questions about her; the drive turned out to be a pleasant, relaxed experience that augured well for the evening. At least this time he hasn't thrown me out of the car, thought Carrie with secret amusement. As they approached the South Bank she realized that she still knew little about the concert they were attending.

"The Academic Festival Overture and the violin concerto by Brahms," he told her when she asked, "and other assorted short pieces."

"Who's the violinist?"

"That's the reason I wanted you to come; he's an old friend of mine, Pavel Bunin."

"Pavel Bunin is a *friend* of yours?" Carrie was astonished. "He's so famous I never imagined him having friends."

Zanov laughed. "He does and I'm one of them. He used to teach me before he defected to the West."

"That must have been when you were a child," said Carrie. "He's been one of the top violinists in the West for at least fifteen years." She was now looking forward to the concert with excitement. Pavel Bunin was her favorite violinist, and it added to the magic occasion that he was actually a friend of Nikolai's.

The concert was everything she had imagined it could be, and more. For the first half of the program she immersed herself in the music; it was an enthusiastic, crowded audience, eager to applaud and appreciate. Everyone was evidently looking forward to the violin concerto that was to conclude the program. At the interval she and Nikolai stood outside on a balcony overlooking the river. To Carrie's amusement Nikolai could name the bridges stretched out sparkling with lights, like floating necklaces reflected in the water—Waterloo, Hungerford, Westminster. He identified Old Scotland Yard, the Shell Building . . .

"And that's Big Ben," said Carrie, laughing. It seemed ridiculous that a Russian should know her own capital city so much better than she did.

Nikolai was relaxed, happy. When the warning bell sounded five minutes before the performance resumed, he took Carrie's glass, put it down, ran his hands lightly up her arms and held her by the shoulders. She felt the same electric tingle she had always felt at his touch, but now she had a deeper knowledge of the joy it promised. His expression told her that his desire for her still burned, and she smiled.

"Don't do anything you might regret," she said teasingly. "The last time you touched me you ended up saying 'I shouldn't have done that.'" She was trying to erase the hurt of his remark, to encourage him to explain it—but his face darkened.

"You're right," he said, and his hands dropped from her shoulders.

Carrie had no doubts about her own feelings. She loved Nikolai. As they returned to their seats she looked forward to the splendid music, a quiet supper,

the drive back to Brighton . . . and then, she thought,
then we'll see.

Two hours later she reflected ruefully on how wrong
she had been about the quiet supper. Bunin's playing
was magnificent, and the crowd had applauded and
stamped, bringing the Russian back again and again to
take bows. When at last the audience began to leave
the hall, Zanov took Carrie by the hand and they
threaded their way in a direction opposite the depart-
ing crowds, down the shallow steps toward the stage.

Backstage at the Festival Hall was a maze of corridors and little rooms, in total contrast to the massive
spaciousness of the main auditorium. Members of the
orchestra were scurrying to and fro, and there was a
crowd of people clustering round Bunin's dressing
room, all talking at the tops of their voices mostly not
in English and drinking Champagne out of paper
cups.

Nikolai pushed his way through them all and finally
greeted Bunin, who was sitting, exhausted, on a
rickety chair in a corner. When he recognized Zanov,
he embraced him warmly and seemed to recover
some energy.

"You must come to the supper," he kept saying.
"Alice is giving a party for me after this—you know,
Theodorovich, the flat near Albert Hall. We can talk
then. Bring the pretty girl—is it Sasha?"

"No," said Zanov. "This is Caroline Astell. She's a
tennis player."

Bunin embraced him again. "I am so happy to see
you. We will talk later, yes?"

Outside, Zanov turned to Carrie. "Do you mind if
we go to this party? I'd like you to meet the hostess,
Lady Alice Bunin, Pavel's brother's wife. She used to

be a friend of my grandmother's, and she's a magnificent old lady, a very good judge of people."

"I'd love to go," said Carrie, since he so evidently looked forward to it. "Will most people at the party speak English, do you think?"

Nikolai laughed. "All of them, if they realize that is your language. Or you can try them in French."

"My French is certainly better than my Russian. Why did he call you Theodorovich? Is that another of your names?"

As they drove across the Thames and down the Strand Nikolai explained the Russian system of names until Carrie begged him to stop. "Just tell me what I should call you," she said.

"Nikolai will do. Just don't be surprised if Russians call me Theodorovich—son of Theodor."

"And come to that," said Carrie, remembering, "why did he call me Sasha? Who was she?"

Zanov hesitated. "Nobody important," he said finally. "A woman I used to know. Pavel is vague over such matters. He was used to seeing me with Sasha, so he assumed you were she."

He wanted to drop the subject, and Carrie knew she couldn't very well continue, though her curiosity was roused. Nikolai didn't speak of Sasha with affection, but rather with contempt. Perhaps their relationship had ended painfully. So Carrie determined to put Sasha out of her thoughts.

Entering Lady Alice Bunin's flat was like stepping back fifty years into another world. The flat itself was huge, a rabbit warren of interconnecting rooms in a building near the Albert Hall; the rooms, high-ceilinged and dimly lit by massive chandeliers, were decorated in red—red flock wallpaper, heavy red velvet curtains. In the gloom Carrie could just make out that the walls were covered with miniatures; row upon row of assorted tiny little paintings, each of them a small delight. The rooms were crowded with people and gilded furniture. A smiling Russian brought them a drink—still Champagne, this time in beautiful fluted glasses. The guests were cosmopolitan, self-assured. As Nikolai led her from group to group she saw faces she recognized—musicians, actors, politicians. He seemed to know most of them but didn't pause to talk. "I want you to meet Alice," he said.

Lady Alice Bunin was sitting on a gilded chair as carved and ornate as a throne. She was an astonishing old woman in her eighties with the remnants of her beauty still evident in her bone structure, her face framed in an aureole of fluffy white hair. Nikolai introduced Carrie, and Alice dismissed the young man she was talking to with an imperious gesture.

"Come and sit here, near me," said the old woman. "Nikolai, go away and meet people—I want to talk to Caroline."

After half an hour of concentrating on Carrie, the old woman closed her eyes. "I am tired," she said. "Fetch Nikolai and tell him."

Carrie worked her way through the crowded rooms to find him deep in conversation with Pavel Bunin. She gave Nikolai the old woman's message, and he went to attend to her.

"Let us get some food," said the musician. "I don't know about you, but playing always makes me hungry." He piled two plates high with food from the buffet and settled them both at a small table, ruthlessly pushing people out of the way to do so. "Don't worry about it," he said, catching Carrie's eye. "Alice's parties are always sink or swim. She asks twice too many guests and then goes to sleep in the middle. I apologize for calling you Sasha. Now I look at you I can see you're years younger, and probably a lot nicer."

"Who was Sasha?"

"Sasha White. An expatriate Russian—Nikolai's girl friend for years. Everyone thought they would marry. Not a nice lady at all. Only interested in herself, I thought. But since you are not her, why should we bother to discuss it?"

Carrie complimented him on his playing, and he laughed. "Thank you, my dear. If things were different in this world of ours, you would have been listening to Nikolai Theodorovich. There—now there was a talent." He shook his head. "Still, who knows? Perhaps it is not yet too late. He cannot go on playing tennis all his life. When he retires, we will see."

Nikolai drove her back to Brighton through deserted roads. Exhausted by a full day of training and the long evening, Carrie settled herself in the soft upholstery of the luxurious car and went to sleep.

When she woke the car was motionless. She blinked and looked around, then realized that it was parked in the stableyard outside Nikolai's flat. The yard and garden looked strange and dreamlike, submerged in the moonlight, and Nikolai's shadowed face watching her was exotic and handsome.

"How long were you going to watch me sleep?" she asked, struggling back to consciousness, suddenly no longer tired but tingling with anticipation. She knew without doubt that they would make love, whatever he had said earlier. She knew from the way he had looked at her all evening, from the way he looked at her now, from the tension that was almost tangible in the chill early morning air between them.

"Aren't you going to ask me in for a cup of coffee?" she said.

"I don't want coffee," said Nikolai. "I want you. Will you come in with me?"

"Yes," said Carrie, and followed him up the stairs and into the bedroom. All the lights were out in the main house. It was very quiet, and the only sound was the breaking waves of the distant ocean. Nikolai removed his black tie, his cuff links. She heard the clink of heavy gold as he placed them on the dressing table. There was at once something domestic and erotic about the simple gesture, an acknowledgment of what they were about to do. She stood absolutely still and waited.

He slipped the straps of her dress off her shoulders and kissed her bare shoulders. His touch sent waves of sensation through her body, intensifying when his hands pushed the dress still further down and cupped her breasts, gently rubbing her hardening nipples with his palms. She raked her fingers through his hair, savoring its thickness and the musklike smell of his aftershave, then pulled his head up so she could kiss his mouth. She felt completely at ease with him and prolonged their kiss, teasing him, closing her lips against his tongue. When the long kiss ended, she was breathless and clinging to him. He slipped the dress down her body, and she stepped out of it and stood, bare-breasted, wearing only a lacy slip and panties, the moonlight just touching her firm curves.

"You look like a silver statue," he said. "No . . . too beautiful for a statue, too alive. You don't know how much I've needed this. All evening I've longed to touch you." Carrie nuzzled against him. The silky feel of his shirt, warmed by his skin, rubbed deliciously against her, and she pressed the length of her body against his.

His response was immediate; she could feel him against her, and her body melted in return, urgent in its need for the pleasure she knew he could give. With trembling fingers she began to undress him; impatient to help her, he took over and removed his clothes.

In seconds he was on the bed kneeling beside her, stroking her flat stomach and sliding her remaining clothes down over her hips, his hand stroking the skin he revealed, his lips brushing hers lightly. She moaned, enjoying the sensations too much to move, yet longing to touch him in return. He stroked her foot, pushing it toward her body so her knee bent outward, baring her inner thigh. He bent his head, brushing her skin with his lips and tongue, slowly and tenderly moving up her leg. The delicate movements of his tongue rippled through her in rising waves of unaccustomed desire, and she couldn't lie still beneath him. She wanted to excite him as he was exciting her, and she stroked the back of his neck, her hands curving around his shoulders, and gently moved herself downward, turning them both over so that she was on top of him.

He stretched his arms behind his head, leaving his body for her to explore, and she savored every moment, her hands caressing his chest, her teeth nibbling gently at his shoulders. She was provoked and tantalized by his immobility, wanting to make him respond, make him show his need for her. She rubbed her legs against his, moving her slender hips against his hard masculinity till he grasped her insistently and thrust himself inside her.

Though she was on top, he was in control, and he

set the rhythm of their movements, which became deeper and deeper until Carrie gasped in uncontrollable pleasure, lost to everything except Nikolai's command of her body, her emotions, herself. There were no doubts as they moved in unison; she knew he loved her, and she was lost in her love for him. They were sharing an intimacy and an intensity of pleasure she had never known.

As their heartbeats slowly returned to normal Nikolai put a protective arm around her. He isn't turning away this time, she thought in a state of dreamy contentment. He was hugging her affectionately, brushing damp strands of golden hair clear of her eyes, and she felt at peace.

"You're not going to say 'I shouldn't have done that' this time, are you?" she murmured.

"I can see you will never let me forget my idle words."

"They weren't idle; that was the trouble. You meant them."

"I was thinking of you, Carrie, believe me. I had no regrets on my own account—how could I?"

Carrie woke at six, still held close to Nikolai's side. As she remembered the night before, pure happiness engulfed her, and the beauty of the morning—sun streaming onto the carpet, delicate sea breeze fluttering the curtains—seemed an echo of the rightness of the love between them. Nikolai hadn't said he loved her, but he'd shown it. Confident in her feminine instinct, Carrie knew she was very important to him. With his arm round her, his sleeping body next to hers, the future seemed assured. Wherever he went, she would go. And if that meant back to Russia . . . She put the thought to the back of her mind. She knew he wanted to stay in the West; only concern for his sister had stopped him from defecting long ago. Surely they could work something out.

Carefully she started to edge her way out of bed. It was time for her morning run. Just as she thought she'd managed to get up without waking Nikolai, he caught her round the waist and pulled her back into bed.

"I have to go," she said when he had kissed her thoroughly. "Training calls."

"You'd rather run than stay in bed with me?" he teased. "Not very flattering."

"Don't fish for compliments." She wriggled away from him. "Plenty of time for bed later. We've got the rest of our lives, remember?" He looked at her face, radiant with confidence and happiness.

"I hope you're right. You don't know how much I want you to be right."

She was moved by his heartfelt words. "It'll work out, Nikolai, you'll see. Are you coming to run?"

"If I can join you in the shower."

"Not likely. You're too big, and you'll take all the water." Carrie dashed for the bathroom, just managing to lock the door against him.

The shower was a delight. She soaped her body under the needlepoints of cold water, remembering Nikolai's admiration of her skin, her breasts, her legs, reveling in her memories and looking forward to days and nights with Nikolai.

At breakfast Tony was in a good mood. He was delighted with Carrie's draw in the singles of the French championship and, not noticing that she was paying very little attention, talked on about her opponents and the tactics she would use in each round. Carrie's calm temperament meant that she never anticipated trouble before it arrived; two hours before each match she played, having worked as hard as she could in preparation, she would listen carefully to Tony's analysis of the tactics she should adopt. She'd accept some ideas, reject others, and then play the match as well as she could. Most of Tony's earlier advice was entirely wasted, as both his wife and his daughter had frequently explained to him, but he still couldn't resist anticipating and savoring every point in advance.

So on this occasion Carrie sipped her coffee and nodded now and then while Betty, preparing a batch of casseroles for the freezer, watched with a twinkle in her eye. Finally she observed dryly, "All you're saying is that Carrie was lucky to avoid Chris Lloyd till the final."

Tony paused, affronted. "I'm saying a great deal more than that," he protested.

"So Nikolai won't be in for breakfast," said Betty to change the subject and give Tony time to smooth his ruffled feathers.

"No, he has business in London," Carrie responded. "Sponsorship talks, I think. He'll be back this afternoon. What do you want me to do this morning, Tony?"

Her father eyed her critically. "You look too tired to do much. How about going to sleep until lunch, and then we'll see?"

Carrie accepted this gratefully and left the kitchen, managing to avoid her mother's eye. She was sure that Betty was worried about her involvement with Nikolai, but she was determined not to let her mother

inveigle her into a heart-to-heart talk. Time enough for
that when Carrie knew her future plans more clearly.

After a long sleep she felt much more rested and no
less happy. Nikolai still hadn't returned from London
at lunch; afterward Carrie drove into Brighton with a
long shopping list and did the rounds of supermarket,
butcher and grocer. On the way back through the
center of Brighton she saw a familiar figure—the
unmistakable bulk of Karel Vronsky. She also recognized the man he was with. It was the man who had
followed her in Rome, the blond with cold blue eyes
whom she called the Frozen Man.

She stopped the car once she was at a safe distance
from them and leaned her head against the steering
wheel. That she must tell Nikolai was her first instinct.
Then another fear struck her. If this man was with
Karel Vronsky, then perhaps he'd been associated
with Nikolai from the beginning. But if so, why hadn't
Nikolai told her so in the car in Rome when she'd
complained she was being followed?

It was too complicated. In England Carrie had been
able to persuade herself that she and Nikolai were two
ordinary people getting to know each other, but now,
it seemed, that process was over for the time being.
Vronsky could only have come for Nikolai.

Her father was working at a pile of papers on the
kitchen table when she arrived. "I thought you were
coaching one of your teenagers now," said Carrie.

"Zanov's looking after him for me," said Tony. "He
said he wanted to relax. I've got these VAT invoices to
do—the Revenue are after us again. Your mother's
down by the courts watching."

She hastened to the court where Nikolai and the
boy were playing. "Come and join me," said Betty,

patting the bench beside her. "Zanov's a good coach as well as a good player—a very rare combination."

Carrie felt too unsettled and apprehensive for a gentle chat about tennis. She sat down and asked: "Will they be finished soon? I want to speak to him."

"Another fifteen minutes." Her mother gave her a swift glance, aware of her tension, but said nothing.

Carrie sat in silence, her anxiety stilled a little by the poetry of the game in front of her. It was a perfect afternoon, the May sun shining on the courts, the dazzling whites standing out against the rich green of the grass. There was a steady sound of ball on racket; Zanov was playing considerately, skillfully, always placing the ball so it was just within the boy's reach. The teenager, Jack Williams, challenged by playing with a champion, was rising to new heights.

"You'll enjoy your doubles matches," commented Betty; "he's magnificent. If I were twenty years younger—"

"If you were twenty years younger I'd be sitting at my drawing board in London," said Carrie, "because you were much better than I'll ever be."

"Won't you tell me what's worrying you?" said Betty. "Is it anything to do with Zanov? You looked so happy this morning, I thought you'd enjoyed your evening with him."

Carrie said nothing, and her mother didn't press. When at last the men's game was over, she spoke as briefly to Jack Williams as politeness allowed before maneuvering herself alone with the Russian and explaining to him about the men she'd seen in Brighton.

He nodded. "It was only a matter of time before Karel found me," he said.

"Before he *found* you? Didn't you tell him where you were going?"

"No, he worked it out for himself. He's not a fool. But so long as I didn't tell him, then he could insist he didn't know."

"Insist? Who to?"

"To the people who want to keep me in order, like the man you call the Frozen Man. He is an agent called Alexei Peters."

Nikolai seemed already distant from her; his eyes were abstracted, calculating. "I shall have to go back now," he said. "They've come to bring me back."

"And you have no choice?"

"Not much. And not much time, either."

"So where will you go now?"

"Paris. It's only three days till the French championships—it wouldn't be worth going back to Russia."

Carrie smiled and tried to look cheerful. "I'll see you on Sunday, then."

"Yes." He hesitated, and then, as if he had made up his mind, began to speak. "Carrie, trust me."

"I do. I always have," said Carrie, "since I got to know you."

"Last night . . ." he began, and Carrie was impatient to hear what he had to say, but the sound of approaching footsteps silenced him.

"Nikolai Theodorovich, how fortunate!" said a voice behind them. Karel and the blond man were approaching, led by Tony. "Mr. Astell kindly told us you were here. Let me introduce myself. I am Alexei Peters . . ."

Carrie hardly listened to the blond man's words, she was so repelled and fascinated by his manner. He seemed both insolent and insinuating, and he eyed her with cold lechery. Meeting him, she no longer felt fearful of the unknown and the unpredictable—but she felt a much more real fear of a person. Karel Vronsky seemed ashamed and sulky; he hardly raised his head to greet Nikolai, and he ignored everyone else, though Alexei ignored this and constantly appealed to him for corroboration. "We very much like the local scenery, isn't that so, Karel? England is a very beautiful country." His light, emotionless voice had a distinct American accent.

Tony Astell was confused; his initial welcoming enthusiasm died as he watched Zanov's evident hostility and Carrie's unhappy silence.

"We won't impose on your hospitality any longer," said Alexei, his eyes flickering from face to face. "Unfortunately, we must leave for Paris straight away. Is that not so, Karel?"

Vronsky muttered something and turned away. "Nikolai Theodorovich will understand. It is better for *everyone*"—he stressed the word slightly, his gaze on Carrie—"if we leave for Paris right away."

"Hello and welcome," said Betty Astell cheerfully, joining them. "Can I offer you tea?"

"Thank you, but no," said Nikolai, picking up his racket and towel from the chair with a note of finality. "Unfortunately we have to leave immediately for Paris."

"So this is good-bye for the moment," said Tony jocularly.

"Good-bye," said Nikolai to Carrie.

"Until Sunday," said Carrie defiantly, and the group of Russians departed, not even Tony making any move to escort them from the house.

"What was going on there?" asked Betty. "You could have cut the atmosphere with a knife. And who was that man?"

A little heartened by her mother's robust attitude,

Carrie said, "That was Alexei Peters. He's odd-looking, isn't he?"

"Poisonous," said Betty. "And I didn't like the way he was looking at you, my girl. He's not a coach, is he?"

"I've never seen him before, but I'd be surprised if he's anything to do with tennis," said Tony. "He looks political to me."

5

Carrie felt lost after Nikolai's departure. It wasn't just that he went so suddenly, nor even the manner of their leave-taking, under Alexei's detached and intimidating gaze, for after all, it was only days till they would certainly meet again, on court at least.

Serving mechanically, again and again, Carrie took stock of her life. She was deeply involved with a man who was subject to political pressures she could only guess at. What decisions should she make about the future? If nothing was to become of their relationship, then the last thing she wanted was to trail around the world meeting Nikolai, playing with Nikolai, hearing about Nikolai, being constantly reminded of her own foolishness and hurt.

He'd warned her again and again that they had no future together; she should expect nothing. For her, their physical relationship was intense, unique. But she felt bound to him more than physically—she knew she loved him. Despite her feelings she was still haunted by the fear that to him she was just another woman—worth traveling from Rome for, of course, but then he gave the impression of being so bored with his tennis-playing life that any diversion would do.

Her mother, sensing her unhappiness, tried to comfort her. She spoke obliquely of the pressures Russian sportsmen were under; she agreed to support Carrie in any decision she made.

Carrie's life was then complicated even further by the arrival of an old friend of the Astells'. Paula Krantz was a determined, successful American woman in her late fifties, high in the ranks of tennis promoters and anxious to add Carrie to her stable of players for next season's American tours.

"You're looking fit," said Paula happily, scrutinizing Carrie closely as she returned to the house from a training run. Paula was settled cozily in the kitchen discussing terms with a delighted Tony. "Keeping her at work, I hope." She was a small woman who loved bright colors. Today she was in an emerald-green suit and a scarlet blouse, her short gray hair brushed upward in a spiky style. Though normally Carrie would have been glad to see her, at the moment she didn't want to think about next year.

"What's all this I hear about Nikolai Zanov? Ducking out of the Italian Open with a torn ligament—so he *said*—and happening to recuperate near a certain lady I won't mention, who's going to be his new doubles partner. What can this mean, I ask myself?" Paula's arch, knowing eyes were fixed on Carrie. "Romance in the air?"

Carrie smiled politely but coolly, and her mother was quick to step into the conversational breach and change the subject.

After dinner that night Carrie could no longer avoid a discussion with her father. "Carrie, I'm thinking of your future. You know our agreement—you pay me fifteen percent of all you earn to be manager and coach—"

"And you put all that money into your fund," interrupted Carrie.

"That's not the point. As your manager I must advise you. Next year could be worth at least a million dollars to you in prize money and sponsorships. Paula knows a cosmetics company in the States that's interested in you. Then I'm sure the rackets manufacturer we're with at the moment will extend the contract to next year, on much more favorable terms. That was a lovely photograph of you holding the rackets after the semifinal in Perugia—you could see the makers' name quite clearly, and that photograph was syndicated all over the world."

"So now they know what tennis rackets to use in Fiji, I suppose," said Carrie, trying not to let herself take the discussion seriously. Tony took the remark as seriously as he took anything to do with tennis.

"I doubt if the photograph got to Fiji. I don't think the game's very big there." His seriousness, his integrity, shamed her into silence.

"I think you'll make at least a million next year. But we have to start negotiating now. Get 'em interested, and when you go storming through the early rounds at Wimbledon, get a good price. But if we're talking about money like that, I think my commission should come down. Fifteen per cent is too much."

"A million is more than Jimmy ever made," said Carrie. "Are you sure I'll be worth that much?"

"With all respect to Jimmy, he's not as pretty as you are. Also, so far he hasn't reached your standard."

Tony was only putting into words what Carrie had half-known for some months, but still his statement was a shock. She'd grown so used to thinking of Jimmy as the tennis star and herself as the understudy, but now their roles were reversed.

"One thing I do know," she said firmly, "is that if any deals are made, you'll get your fifteen per cent. No, don't argue. Think what the fund could do with the money."

"But do I have your permission to make arrangements for next year?"

"Tony, I don't know. I'll give you an answer in Paris. Just give me a few days."

Reluctantly he accepted this. Carrie had made up her mind to talk to Zanov as soon as she could, to ask him—and why shouldn't she?—exactly what she meant to him.

Tony was in high spirits as they arrived at the small Paris hotel where they always stayed. Despite his intense Englishness, he loved France; he spoke the language fluently though with a strong English accent, and he thoroughly approved of French food, French umpiring—"no crowd ever intimidated a French umpire"—and the Stade Roland Garros, where the championships were held—"at least here most of the paying customers can see and the players don't have to change in pigpens." And lastly, he had high hopes for Carrie's success. He always took charge of the rackets and shoes; as they unpacked he checked and rechecked the equipment, humming tunelessly to himself and sometimes breaking into song. He wandered in and out of Carrie's room.

"I wonder where Jimmy is?" he remarked on his fourth or fifth visit. Jimmy had arrived in Paris from

Rome three days ago and was staying at the same hotel, but there was no sign of him in his room, and he hadn't left a message.

"Probably interviewing some player for his newspaper," suggested Carrie. She longed to be alone to try to get in touch with Zanov; she could find his hotel by telephoning the tournament organizers, and Tony's evident pleasure in anticipating the deals he could negotiate on her behalf was making her feel guilty.

Eventually she suggested they go downstairs for tea. The hotel specialized in English visitors and prided itself on providing an English tea—a delicious snack of French cakes and delicately flavored tea—light years away from the English meal. As they were eating Jimmy burst into the room, full of exuberance and information. He and Tony were soon deep in a conversation; Carrie, having registered that they were talking tennis, only half-listened, wondering when she could escape upstairs to her room.

"And you'll never guess whom I just interviewed," said Jimmy. "Nikolai Zanov, no less. He told me all about his stay at our place in Brighton."

"Oh?" said Carrie, her attention caught. "Was a blond man called Alexei with him?"

"No, only Sasha. She's a lovely girl, and very nice. She was really kind to me and gave me lots of information before he came in."

"Who?" said Tony, with a glance at his daughter.

"Sasha White. Don't you remember her? She went everywhere with Zanov a year or two back. Blond girl, tall, beautiful body. They're together again, she tells me."

"Are you sure?" asked Carrie through stiff lips that would hardly shape the words.

"It certainly looks like it. They're sharing a suite at

the hotel, anyway. Besides, everyone's talking about it. I had it in confidence from Mireille Villefour that they're going to be married. They've been absolutely inseparable over the weekend; she watches him practice—he's fit again, by the way, good thing for you, Carrie—and they hold hands and gaze into each other's eyes."

Carrie felt sick. Her father gave Jimmy a warning glance, but he simply plowed on. "You'll see them at the official reception tonight, anyway. You accepted the invitation, didn't you? And I'm going as press. Bring on the day when I'll go as a player."

"I think I'll go upstairs and rest," said Carrie, her voice surprising her by its normality, as if another person were speaking. She had forgotten the reception that evening; she'd been happy to go last week when Tony was replying to the invitations; she had looked forward to it, knowing that Nikolai would be there and half-expecting him to take her out for dinner afterward.

"What's the matter with Carrie?"

"Just tired, I expect," said Tony, knowing she would prefer her personal affairs kept private.

Later Tony knocked on Carrie's door.

"Come in." She was sitting in front of the dressing-table mirror, putting the final touches to her makeup. She had dressed with care; her hair was piled on top of her head in a more formal style than she usually wore; her dress, strapless black moiré with a tight bodice and a knee-length full skirt, emphasized the length of her legs and the smoothness of her shoulders.

"I was going to ask you if you were sure you wanted to go to this party," he said, "but I have my answer. You look very beautiful, my dear."

"A father's prejudice," Carrie said lightly, and kissed him, comforted by his care for her.

The party was held in another hotel near the Champs-Elysées. Normally it would have been a happy evening for Carrie. She knew almost all the players and liked many of them; but for the first hour, though she moved from group to group and made appropriate responses to people, she was tense and apprehensive, waiting for Zanov to appear with or without the famous Sasha White.

"Hi," said Dallas Parfitt, tapping her on the shoulder and making her jump. "I like your dress."

This attempt at social chat over, Dallas launched into a discussion of their first-round women's doubles match; they were drawn against two comparatively obscure Australian players. Carrie tried to listen to Dallas's words, but she couldn't make sense of them. She kept her eyes fixed on the doorway through which the guests arrived. Each time a man entered, she was sure it was Nikolai. Then, when she was tired of waiting and relaxed her attention for a moment, she realized he was in the room already; she could hear his voice, not far from her.

He was standing talking to two French officials; next to him, her hand possessively on his arm, was a woman who could only be Sasha White. Even Carrie had to admit that she was striking, but together they did not give an impression of relaxed happiness. It was more a jailer's than a lover's grip she held him in, thought Carrie, then dismissed the idea as jealousy.

Zanov finished talking to the officials and turned away. Carrie caught his eye; he smiled at her politely, as if she were a distant acquaintance, and she was cut to the heart, her warm and spontaneous smile of welcome congealing on her lips.

Sasha spoke to him in an intimate undertone, evidently inquiring who Carrie was; he answered, and the woman laughed.

"Good evening, Nikolai," said Carrie, approaching, determined not to be put off. Common politeness dictated that she acknowledge him.

"Good evening," he replied. "Sasha, I don't think you've met my doubles partner, Caroline Astell. Caroline, this is Sasha White." His face was emotionless. Carrie searched it in vain for some hint that he understood her bewilderment at the sudden appearance of this woman from his past. Sasha looked down at Carrie. She was a tall, slim woman in a clinging black dress that contrasted with her very blond hair, white grin and startlingly red lips, and though Carrie had felt satisfied with her own appearance till that moment, she now felt too short and too brown.

"How nice to meet you," said Sasha in a deep, husky voice with a trace of a German accent. "I hope you are good at tennis, if you are to play with Nikolai. He likes to win." These apparently innocuous words were spoken in a tone of patronizing contempt, and Carrie could think of no reply. The trio stood in silence for a moment; then Sasha said, "Come on, darling, introduce me to some interesting people," and Carrie was left alone with very uncharitable thoughts.

Later, as she was waiting in the ladies' room for her coat, Sasha materialized beside her. She moves just like a snake, thought Carrie.

"We meet again—I'm sorry, what is your name?"

Carrie was sure that this ignorance was feigned and didn't respond.

"Jane?" wondered Sasha. "Or perhaps Jackie? I wouldn't have thought Samantha—you don't seem a

Samantha, somehow. Still, never mind, it doesn't really matter. I'm always glad to meet Nikolai's fans."

Carrie smiled.

"Nikolai tells me *everything*," the older woman went on. "What he thinks, what he feels— everything."

"How nice for you," murmured Carrie, thinking, *Liar*.

"And he's told me how you pursued him in Rome. So I just thought I'd warn you—now I'm back, he won't have any time to spare for other women."

"How nice for him."

"And dear Alexei doesn't approve of you."

"The feeling is mutual," said Carrie coolly.

"Oh, no, don't say that," warned Sasha. "It doesn't do to make an enemy of Alexei. He's been known to be quite . . . ruthless."

"I'm not surprised," said Carrie, taking her coat from the uniformed maid, relieved to get away.

The cloakroom was at the end of a narrow corridor. As she closed the door of the cloakroom behind her, she saw Alexei standing in the corridor, unavoidable. He was blocking the passage, and she stopped a few feet away, reluctant to approach.

"Good evening," he said. She made to pass him, and he put his arm across the corridor just at shoulder height, barring her way. She stopped so close to him that she could feel his breath on her cheek. He dropped his hand on her bare shoulder and rested it there. Instinctively she shrank away from him, and his fingers tightened, pressing into her flesh with a dominant insistence.

Suddenly Carrie was angry. She willed herself to keep still and said coldly: "If you don't take your hand from my shoulder I shall scream."

He dropped his hand, still standing close to her, his eyes with their pale lashes only inches from her own.

"Would you let me pass, please?"

"Why not?"

Sasha came up behind her. Carrie looked from one to the other—the same smiling, remote, clear-cut features, the same dead blue eyes. How could Nikolai ever have loved this woman? And why was he with her now?

Later she lay sleepless in the old-fashioned room of her hotel, trying to find a comfortable place in the creaking bed and watching the lights from passing cars in the street outside reflect on the ceiling in ever-changing patterns. Was it wishful thinking to hope that Nikolai still had any feeling for her? Surely their lovemaking could not be so easily forgotten, could not be completely dismissed. She didn't believe that. He had shown her such tenderness, taken her with such passion. It had been as real for him as for her, she was sure. But even if he was being watched by his keeper Alexei, if he had wanted to give her a glance to show that he was not with Sasha by choice, he certainly could have done so. Perhaps it would be shutting her eyes to the obvious if she continued to hope she meant anything to him.

As the long night dragged on she tried to concentrate on tennis, to think her way through her singles match the following day. Her opponent, an unseeded Dutch player, was a thirty-five-year-old veteran with her best games well behind her, but Carrie knew that she must never underestimate an opponent. All her efforts could not distract her from thoughts of Nikolai, however, and it was dawn before she fell into an uneasy sleep and dreamed of Sasha White.

At breakfast Jimmy was in high spirits. Tony had agreed to let him stay on in Paris for the tournament if he could arrange for a coach to take his place at the Astell school; he'd found a satisfactory replacement and was rejoicing. Besides that, he was full of gossip from the reception, and he especially sang the praises of Sasha. Carrie drank orange juice, forced herself to eat the scrambled eggs Tony had ordered especially for her, and wished with all her heart that Jimmy had more tact and more sense.

Tony could only endure so much of Jimmy's hymns to Sasha. "That will do," he said firmly. "That woman belongs to Zanov, you tell me, so don't go hanging around her. Besides, she looks perfectly ordinary to me. A bit hard-faced and longer in the tooth than she'll admit. I don't want to hear any more about her."

Jimmy heard the determination in his father's voice and obeyed; all Carrie heard was "That woman belongs to Zanov," and every fiber of her being rebelled against it. It doesn't make sense, she thought bitterly. None of it makes sense.

For the first week of the French championships Carrie needed all her self-control and determination not to allow her feelings to show. She felt more hurt than she imagined possible, and as she saw Nikolai every day, always with Sasha in attendance, it was impossible for her to put the whole matter out of her mind. She was also worried by his tennis; it was lifeless, without fire or interest. He was just scraping through to win against opponents who would normally not have interrupted the smooth flow of his progress toward the final.

Carrie's own play was improving. The predictability and physical effort of a tennis match was actually a relief. Not only did she win her first- and second-round singles matches, she and Dallas had no problem dismissing the Australian women in straight sets.

Her last match of the week was a mixed doubles second-round match. Nikolai and she had skipped the first round when the man of their opponents' partnership was injured. Now they were playing Mireille Villefour and a veteran Frenchman; the crowd was naturally supporting their own countrymen, but neither Carrie nor Nikolai was bothered by the crowd. On record they should have no trouble in winning.

When she arrived in the waiting room, only Nikolai was there. He was standing at the window looking out, his shoulders hunched, every line of his muscular body defiant. So powerful was the impression of controlled anger that Carrie hesitated to approach him.

"Nikolai," she said, and he nodded without turning round.

Hurt, resenting his treatment of her, Carrie struggled to pull herself together and discuss tactics. "You serve first," she said, "and I'll take the left-hand court. I'll take the net and you cover the baseline. Okay?"

He nodded again, and Carrie joined him at the window. A men's singles match was in progress on the court next to theirs. "McEnroe's in good form," said Carrie, needling him with small talk, standing so close to him she could almost feel the heat of his body in the white track suit. He grunted, neither in agreement or disagreement.

"We could withdraw, you know," she pointed out. "There's practically no money in it, and now that we're both into the third round of the singles, next week is going to be very hard."

"What do you want to do?" he said, his back to her.

She shrugged. "Usually I'd say, we've entered, so

we should play. But if you're going to be so . . ." She hesitated.

"So what?"

"So—so miles away, so hostile, so *rude!*" said Carrie, finally goaded beyond endurance. "I'd rather not play."

Even as she spoke she knew it was a lie; she knew that she would prefer to see Nikolai, to be with him on court, and at least have a chance of finding out what was really going on.

"We should play," he said. "It is too late to withdraw. See, the officials are coming to get us."

As he spoke their French opponents entered the waiting room to a flurry of greetings and polite remarks; then they were being led onto the court.

As Carrie settled her rackets and towels by the umpire's chair, she studied the crowd; nearly every seat was filled, and she could see Sasha in a front-row seat talking animatedly to Alexei.

The first set was disastrous. Carrie tried to concentrate, but she was ruffled and angry, and her game suffered. Nikolai appeared completely indifferent and repeatedly hit shots into the net or out of court. The French pair won six-two. Then Nikolai held his service and they changed ends at one-love.

"We're losing," said Carrie. "Why don't you do something about it?"

"Does it matter?" said Zanov. He'd put in so little effort that after nine games he wasn't even sweating.

"Yes, it does," said Carrie. "These people have paid to watch us. Besides, I feel a fool running for the shots you should take."

He gave a reluctant smile. "Would it please you to win?"

"Yes."

"I'll see what I can do. Come on, our minute is up."

Sasha was waving at Zanov. He acknowledged her greeting with a nod of the head.

"Are you enjoying your stay in Paris?" asked Carrie, resolved to try and break through the wall of silence between them.

He looked at her, looked at Sasha, looked at her again. "What do you think?" he said.

"I don't know. How should I know?"

"Our minute is up," he said again, and returned to the court.

They won the next set six-one, and the final set was a formality: with Nikolai concentrating there was no hope for the French pair.

"Thank you," said Carrie when the match ended.

"Any time," said Zanov, and walked off with a wave of his hand. By the time she showered and changed, he'd left, and there was no sign of Jimmy.

Saturday was free, and Carrie set out on her own to buy tickets for a concert. She had decided to make one last effort with Nikolai. She would find a suitable concert that evening; she would buy two tickets for it, and she would invite him to join her. She returned to the hotel at lunchtime with a new dress and tickets to hear Tchaikovsky's violin concerto played by a totally unfamiliar Frenchman and an orchestra she had never heard of in a hall in an obscure quarter of Paris.

Armed with those, she visited Zanov's hotel, asked for him to be paged and waited in the foyer. She'd almost decided he wasn't there when he appeared with Alexei at his side.

"Can I speak to you alone?" she said to Nikolai.

"I really don't think that would be wise," said Alexei.

"Please," said Carrie, ignoring the blond Russian.

"Things are difficult at the moment," said Nikolai. "As you can see, I'm pressed for time."

Obviously Alexei was not going to leave, and Carrie decided to behave as if he weren't there. "It's just that I have tickets for a concert tonight, and as it's a rest day tomorrow, I wondered if you'd like to come with me."

"That is kind," said Alexei, "but I don't think Sasha likes music."

"I wasn't asking Sasha."

"Ah, well"—he spread his hands regretfully—"then Nikolai Theodorovich certainly would not be able to come. He and Sasha are inseparable."

"Is that true, Nikolai?"

"He has . . . commitments, responsibilities," said Alexei in a warning tone, and Zanov checked what he had been about to say. "Now I myself am free this evening," he continued. "I would be delighted to accept your kind invitation. I am myself a music lover, a man of sensitivity and artistic interests."

He was laughing at her, Carrie was sure, but he was serious about coming to the concert. She cast an appealing look at Nikolai, but his face was stony.

"Do not look so downcast, Carrie," Alexei went on. "I hate to see such a beautiful young lady downcast. I have said, I will be delighted to accompany you."

"I'd rather go with a snake," said Carrie. He caught her wrist in a firm grip.

"That's not polite," he said reprovingly, and Carrie stamped her high heel into his instep with all the combined force of her anger and precision. His coolness deserted him, and he hopped about, cursing.

Carrie turned and left the foyer, head held high. When she reached the door, she turned; Alexei was still moaning, and Nikolai was watching her with a smile of pure delight.

But once she was out in the street, the brief moment of pleasure in getting at least some measure of revenge on Alexei left her. It had started to rain, and she wasn't wearing a coat. She sought the shelter of a nearby café and ordered a drink she didn't want.

The café was an elegant one, just off the Champs-Elysées; at this time of the afternoon most of the patrons were Americans, Germans and Frenchwomen so elegant, so well turned out, it was impossible to tell what they actually looked like. Carrie looked around rather anxiously for Paula Krantz. It was exactly the sort of place she frequented.

The American woman couldn't be dodged for long, in any case; she and Tony were having dinner together on the following day, and Carrie knew she would have to make up her mind by then about the arrangements for next year. At least now she knew that she had to leave Nikolai out of her calculations. Whatever he felt for her, it seemed clear he might not have the freedom to make a commitment to her.

She wandered back to her hotel, more upset than she realized, in what was virtually a state of shock, went up to her room, lay on the bed and fell into an exhausted sleep.

When she woke, someone was knocking on the door and calling out, "Carrie! Carrie!"

"Come in," she said, still half-asleep, and Jimmy bounded into the room.

"It's dark in here," he said, drawing the curtains back. She shrank away from the light. "Anything wrong? Not like you to rest in the middle of the day—Just came to ask you, Ben Jackson and I are going out for dinner tonight, and we wondered if you and Dallas would like to come."

Carrie shook her head.

"Oh, come on, Carrie. You've been a blight all this week—I don't know what's got into you—and it'll do you good to get out. And it would really please Ben. He's worried about you, and you know how important you are to him. Besides, I want to celebrate."

"What?" said Carrie.

"I've got the reports from the doctor in London this morning. He says it's all clear with the knee. I can start training immediately. By next year, who knows? I'll probably be back in big-time tennis. Six months should make some difference. I'll be catching up with you!"

Carrie looked at him with affection. Despite his insensitivity and loudness, he was basically very good-natured and was not in the least jealous of his sister—which, under the circumstances, would have been understandable.

"By all means I'll celebrate your knee," said Carrie. "Just not tonight, Jimmy."

He sat down on the bed beside her. "There is something the matter, isn't there? And now and then this week I've wondered if it isn't to do with me. You've given me some very odd looks at times. Did you not like my being in Paris watching you; was that it?"

Carrie made up her mind to explain a little about her relationship with Nikolai, so that Jimmy might get the hint and stop mentioning Sasha quite so much.

He listened to her account in silence.

When she finished, he burst out, "But that's monstrous, Carrie! He treated you—he treated you—"

"Don't be angry, Jimmy, it's not like that. Whatever's gone wrong, I don't think it was Nikolai's doing. I get the impression he's being held in a sort of blackmail. Otherwise he wouldn't be with Sasha, I'm sure of it."

She had touched a nerve in Jimmy. "Oh, no," he denied with absolute conviction, "you're quite wrong there. He begged Sasha to come back to him. He absolutely begged her; she told me all about it."

Carrie saw that it was useless to attempt any explanation that put Sasha in a less than favorable light.

"But you must come out to dinner tonight," urged Jimmy. "Ben will help take your mind off Zanov. You're better off without that Russian. He's just a phony. He puts on temper tantrums when he's losing; I've watched him do it. Gamesmanship, to cover up the fact he's nearly past it." Carrie thought, but did not say, that Nikolai was currently ranked number three in the world while Jimmy at his best had only managed seventy-five. She now regretted telling her brother anything about Nikolai, but it was too late. She wasn't going to spend the evening with him and Ben Jackson, that was certain.

The next morning she knew she would have to make a decision about contracts for next year—and when it came to the point there was hardly a decision to be made. To deny Tony the opportunity of seeing one of his greatest dreams come true, now that he was actually in sight of being coach and manager to a British player who was also an international star, would take more detachment than Carrie ever possessed. Her father had spent days, months, years, developing her talent, and she couldn't cheat him now.

The decision made, she felt better. By next year, who knew? She may have forgotten all about Nikolai Zanov, she told herself without in the least believing it. Her father's reception of the news was all she had hoped. He was obviously delighted and, apart from thanking her, made no attempt to discuss her feelings or sympathize with her.

Paula Krantz was not equally tactful. "There you are," she said, cornering Carrie after dinner as she tried to slip through the hotel lounge unobserved. "Your father and I have made a deal and I can honestly say you'll be a richer woman for it."

So will you, thought Carrie. "I'm sure you've been fair," she said.

"More than fair—isn't that so, Tony?" Tony said nothing, but Carrie could see that he was pleased with himself. Paula regarded them both with her usual lively curiosity. "Odd about Sasha White turning up again," she said. "Now, I'd have bet a substantial sum of money that those two were through. I'd have sworn he was interested in someone quite different, wouldn't you, Carrie?"

"I never thought about it," lied Carrie, trying to decide whether Paula was being deliberately unkind or just insensitive and selfish.

"You're the only one, in that case," said Paula. "All Paris is talking about it."

Carrie laughed. "Come on, Paula! Not *all* Paris. Most of Paris is utterly indifferent to anything to do with tennis, and of the people who know about tennis, only a few are interested in idle gossip."

"My, my," said Paula. "I never knew you had claws, Carrie."

"Drop it, Paula," said Tony. "We should celebrate, not argue. Have a glass of wine with us, Carrie."

The small rift was smoothed over; with elephantine tact Paula avoided the subject of Zanov, and they managed to find enough small talk to fill half an hour, after which Carrie felt justified in taking her leave. But Paula's words still rankled, and the next day, while she and Dallas were waiting to go on court for a practice, she questioned the American girl.

"Have you heard anything about me and Nikolai Zanov?"

Dallas, blessedly unreflective, didn't find this an unusual question. "Not that I can recall. Oh, yes, wait a minute . . . I heard something. I know what it was—about the match on Friday. Zanov was right off his game and you gave him a talking to and you pulled back from one set down to get the match. Is that what you mean?"

"Near enough."

Not that Dallas was exactly aware of everything that went on around her, thought Carrie, but she was probably typical of the average tennis player.

6

〰〰〰〰〰〰〰

Women's semifinal day proved unpleasantly hot and humid. Carrie was due to play at two o'clock, and Tony waited with her for the officials to arrive and fetch the players. He was chatting about the tennis school; Carrie suddenly realized how unusual this was. "You're not telling me how to play the match," she interrupted. "Aren't you going to?" Normally he was beside her giving instructions till the last minute.

He took her hand. "It has occurred to me lately," he said, "that you don't listen to most of my advice. Eh?"

Carrie smiled. "You know I respect your opinion."

"That's as may be, but you follow your own judgment. Good luck, girl," he called after her as she was led away by a fussy, pompous little Frenchman who insisted on practicing his fractured English on Carrie and her opponent.

They were playing on a comparatively new show court. All the four thousand seats were filled, and the murmur of the crowd was like a huge, friendly domestic animal. Carrie's opponent, a young American girl, seeded number three in the tournament, sucked the braces on her teeth and hit ferocious, unreturnable two-handed shots.

This is supposed to be a warm-up, thought Carrie. What is the game going to be like? But as the first set wore on and she repeatedly changed the tempo of the play, refusing to allow the other girl to settle into a slugging match, she gradually drew ahead and won the first set six-four. The appreciative crowd applauded and cheered for so long that though it wasn't an official break, Carrie had time to look at the players' seats to see who was watching her. She expected Tony, of course, and Dallas; possibly Jimmy and Ben.

But there, sitting in a corner, alone, was Nikolai. When she caught sight of him, she thought she must be mistaken—he was known for never, never watching other players. But it was him.

As the second set progressed she was quite unable to concentrate. Why was he watching her? Surely it meant that he was interested in her, that he cared for her. It could only mean that.

She tried to regain her concentration, but it was impossible. A series of disastrous double faults lost her the second set, and she was so thoroughly ruffled by this that her game disintegrated and it was a cheerful young American who shook hands with her half an hour later.

"I thought you had me beaten, for sure," she admitted frankly. "Whatever happened to you?"

Carrie's eyes sought the players' seats, but Nikolai had gone.

"Come on, Carrie," said Ben that evening in the lounge of the hotel. "Sitting here and moping won't help. Let's go out and have dinner—or would you prefer a cinema? They're bound to have subtitles, aren't they?"

"The last thing I want to do is go to the cinema," said Carrie. "Food, yes. So long as it's only you and me and I don't have to make an effort."

"Do you want to go anywhere special?"

"No," said Carrie, "let's just walk and choose a restaurant we like the look of."

It began as a pleasant evening. They strolled through a park, then through cobbled streets toward the center of Paris, where Ben waited patiently, hands in pockets, while Carrie window-shopped.

"Isn't this very tedious for you?" she asked when eventually she joined him and they walked in search of a restaurant.

"You are never tedious. I'd rather be with you than anyone else."

His dogged devotion made her feel guilty, and his choice of an expensive restaurant and the care he took over the food and wine made it worse. He wanted to know about her arrangements for next season, and she told him a little about Paula Krantz and the American cosmetics sponsorship.

"That's marvelous! You're all set now; there'll be no holding you, especially when you win the mixed doubles at Wimbledon. You and Zanov could, you know."

Every mention of Nikolai rubbed salt in Carrie's

emotional wounds. The days in Brighton, the magical closeness that he and Carrie had shared, now seemed infinitely remote, another world of hope and happiness. She was oppressed by a feeling of loss. There she was in a good restaurant eating delicious food with a man who cared for her—if only she didn't feel so empty, so lost, so mechanical and lifeless. Even the food, tasteless, stuck in her throat, and the waiters took away course after course hardly touched.

Ben's concerned expression made her feel still more guilty, and she attempted apology, but he wouldn't hear of it. "You can't help how you feel, and if you don't want the food, don't eat it."

"But you've taken such trouble—"

"I'm enjoying myself. Don't worry about me."

It was a relief when the bill was paid and they could leave. The night was still warm, and Carrie wanted to walk back. Their way took them past Zanov's hotel; Carrie couldn't resist peering in through the plate-glass windows to the lounge inside, blazing with lights and full of people on display. So intent on looking in, she didn't see Nikolai and Sasha, who were walking along the street toward them until Sasha said, "It's the English girl! Hello, my dear, are you quite recovered?"

"What from?" said Carrie, feeling that enough was quite enough and she wouldn't let Sasha get away with needling her any more.

"Oh," said the other woman, arching her delicate brows slightly. "That disastrous defeat today."

"What disastrous defeat?"

Sasha waved her slim hand with its painted nails in an impatient gesture. "Have you lost two matches today, then?"

Zanov was watching the exchange between the two

women without apparent interest. He was looking tired and drawn, Carrie noticed with a pang of sympathy, and a look of relief crossed his face when she and Ben moved on in a flurry of good nights.

Picking her way carefully over the cobbled streets, Ben's friendly arm supporting her, Carrie thought about Nikolai. Even if for some reason connected with his sister and the Russian authorities he had to do what he was told by Alexei and allow Sasha to be with him at all times, she didn't understand why he didn't at least tell Carrie that he was under duress, that his behavior was not his own choice. Why did he pretend even to her that there was nothing between them?

Perhaps, she thought when at last Ben left her alone, perhaps she was imagining it all. Perhaps Nikolai had at first felt an interest in her that had completely vanished when Sasha, the real love of his life, reappeared.

Every fiber of her being rejected that idea. Sasha was such a poisonous woman. You're just jealous, she told herself. She's certainly beautiful. Jimmy likes her . . . Nikolai loved her. . . .

It was an insoluble puzzle.

"Mixed doubles semifinal," said Tony. "You should enjoy this one. It's just for fun, and if Zanov plays reasonably well—"

"And if I play reasonably well," interrupted Carrie, "not like that disaster in the singles—"

"We agreed to forget that," said Tony, who had his own, correct explanation of his daughter's extraordinary lapse of form on the previous day, and who wished that Nikolai Zanov had never had anything to do with her.

"You'll play very well indeed," said Tony. "Pity about the women's doubles." She and Dallas had withdrawn; the American girl had the flu.

Paris was drab and gray, the suburbs depressing under overcast skies as a taxi took them to the stadium; Carrie expected to have to wait for the match because Zanov had to play a singles semifinal first and then have his break. But she found the singles semifinal had been canceled: Nikolai had withdrawn on the grounds of illness, but was proposing to play the mixed doubles.

All the officials were scurrying about in an uproar; the crowd, waiting to see a promising singles between Zanov and McEnroe, were stamping and shouting complaints. The mixed doubles was scheduled to take place on the same court, and Carrie was appalled at the prospect of having to face such a hostile crowd. They certainly wouldn't understand how a player could be fit enough to play one match, the less-important match, and not another, and they would show their displeasure forcibly.

"Please, this way." A French official ushered Tony and Carrie into a small office that already contained Karel Vronsky, looking miserable; Alexei, smiling; Nikolai, staring moodily out of the window; two French Federation of Tennis officials, and a Grand Prix supervisor. The latter, a tough-looking American, was shrugging his shoulders. "I understand your difficulty with the crowd, monsieur," he said to the senior French official, "but if Mr. Zanov doesn't think he can manage five sets of singles but can manage three sets of doubles, then what do you expect me to say? I can't make him play. It's one of those things, that's all."

"We will get you a doctor, Monsieur Zanov,"

appealed the French official wretchedly. "We will get you the best doctor in Paris."

"I'm not playing," said Zanov flatly. "And McEnroe's gone back to his hotel, anyway."

"But the *crowd!*" said the official, wringing his hands in a gesture Carrie had previously only read about. "The crowd!"

"If I were you I'd get on with it," said the American. "Give them something to watch."

"But they will not like Monsieur Zanov to play the doubles; they are angry," said the wretched official.

"What about the other mixed-doubles semifinal?" suggested another Frenchman.

"We need one of the other singles semifinalists for that."

"That is it, then," said the senior Frenchman. "I'd like the players on court as soon as possible."

Tony looked at his daughter. "What do you think, Carrie?" It was still an hour before she was scheduled to play, and she had the right to insist on waiting.

"The crowd will be worse if they have to wait, won't they? I think we should start now. What about our opponents; are they here?"

Apparently they were, and ready to go on court, so Carrie hurried to change and soon was on court facing a barrage of hostile shouts.

"They're not throwing anything yet," she said to Zanov. "Do you think they will?"

"Not if we manage to give them a good game. Thank your lucky stars you're not in South America; the crowds there would be shooting us by this time."

"Are you really ill?"

"Yes, I think I've got the 'flu."

"Then you're crazy to play. Why did you?"

Zanov didn't reply, and the umpire called the end of the warm-up time.

It took their opponents only an hour to beat them. Despite all Carrie's efforts, she couldn't win the match alone, and she soon saw that Zanov was indeed ill. Fortunately the crowd gradually also came to see it, and when the match was over, the applause, though rather grudging, was an improvement on the hostility that had greeted them. Photographers surrounded the winning pair; Nikolai and Carrie stood a little apart.

"Why did you play?" she asked again, but he just shook his head.

"That man you were with last night . . ."

"Ben? He's a friend of Jimmy's."

"And a friend of yours."

"Yes."

"He looks at you as if he loves you," said Nikolai.

"Maybe he does," said Carrie. "Does it matter?" Although thousands of people could see them, no one was paying any attention to them. All eyes were on the winners; Carrie felt as if they were alone. "Do you remember the night we went to the Festival Hall?"

"Of course I remember," he said, pulling a sweater over his sodden shirt. "But you must not. Ben looks like a nice man."

"He is, but we're not talking about Ben. We're talking about you and me. You can't be jealous of Ben; it's ridiculous."

Nikolai looked at her. "You must understand, Carrie. He is free. I am not. I want you. So I am angry at circumstances."

"And taking it out on Ben," said Carrie. "What do you mean, you're not free?"

"I can't explain. I'm trying to protect you," said Nikolai.

"Please don't. Tell me the truth. I'm not a child."

Before Nikolai could answer, Karel Vronsky joined them and with a curt nod to Carrie swept Nikolai away, murmuring in Russian. Carrie, who might have found Nikolai's words upsetting, was instead heartened by the feeling behind them. The photographer who snapped her as she left the court got the prettiest, happiest Carrie Astell photograph of the whole tournament.

"Grass," said Tony, fastening his seat belt as the plane taxied into position for takeoff. "Thank heavens for that! No more artificial surfaces for a bit. Just wholesome English grass."

"On which I'll probably get a wholesome English damaged knee, like Jimmy," said Carrie. She and her mother always teased Tony about his dogged loyalty to the traditional tennis surface. But his enthusiasm refused to be crushed; he was in an excellent mood, encouraging Carrie to eat all she wanted and chatting away about the prospects at Chichester and Eastbourne, calculating and recalculating, then crowing over Carrie's point total for the season so far in the women's tennis series.

Carrie herself was in a good mood. For one thing, Jimmy wasn't traveling with them. She was trying to keep out of his way to avoid a full-blown fight and telling him what she thought of him. For another, she was looking forward to two uncomplicated weeks playing in the women-only tournaments at Chichester and Eastbourne. She liked playing within traveling distance of home. Hotels were dull after a time.

But in the semifinal of the Chichester tournament, her joking words to Tony came true. She stretched for a ball, skidded and twisted her ankle on the grass.

"Rest," said the doctor. "You must rest that ankle for at least three days. No walking about at all. Then no playing for at least a week."

"No Eastbourne?" Carrie was disappointed.

"Nothing till Wimbledon," said the doctor.

So there it was. "Never mind," said Betty. "Think how much worse it could have been." Her own career had ended with a broken ankle that gave her trouble even now.

Carrie stayed in bed for three days, fretting from the inactivity, reading and rereading thrillers that failed to hold her attention.

The day she was allowed up, Jimmy returned from London. Halfway through dinner, when most of the tennis gossip was exhausted, Jimmy said, "I met Angela Jackson at Queen's Club yesterday."

"Oh?" Angela, Ben's mother, was a pleasant woman and a friend of Betty's.

"And she gave me a message for you, Carrie. An invitation. She wants you to come up to London tomorrow and stay with them for a few days before Wimbledon. She thought you wouldn't be in hard training for a day or two, because of your ankle."

The invitation really came from Ben, of course, but Carrie was tempted to accept. It would be a way of getting up to London without having to go through an advice session from her mother. Carrie had felt during the last few days that Betty was watching her, ready to pounce on any mention of Nikolai; and it was the half-conviction that her mother was right and that she should keep away from the Russian for his sake if not for her own that made Carrie particularly reluctant to talk about it.

"That's a good idea," said Tony heartily. "I'll give you a diet sheet, Carrie, and a list of exercises for that ankle—and mind you eat all the food on my list. You've lost weight this week, and I want to see you built up."

"Mind you have a nice quiet time," said Betty pointedly, and Carrie smiled, pretending not to understand that her mother was warning her to keep out of Nikolai's way.

"I always enjoy staying with the Jacksons," she replied sweetly. "Oh?" said her mother, unconvinced.

Carrie made arrangements with Angela Jackson that evening and packed as soon as she put the phone down. At eight thirty the next morning she'd finished breakfast under Tony's eagle gaze and, still feeling slightly sick from the bowl of muesli he'd made her eat, was on the road to London.

The Jacksons' flat was on the fifth floor of a massive complex built in the nineteen thirties. The long, narrow corridors, deeply carpeted, and the thirties-style cornices all contributed to the total effect. It was just like an ocean liner.

Angela answered the door. "Good, it's you," she said, taking Carrie's suitcase. "Are you supposed to be resting the ankle or what?"

"Not really. I'm to use it as much as possible in normal situations for a day or two without running or playing tennis. After that it should be quite normal."

"You sit yourself down on the sofa and I'll make us a cup of tea," said Angela. "And I'll put your suitcase in your usual room."

Carrie relaxed on the sofa, more tired by the drive than she'd expected, and listened to the peaceful domestic noises Angela was making in the kitchen. Soon the older woman reappeared with a tray and began pouring out tea. "A strange man telephoned asking for you this morning, by the way. He said he was Pavel Bunin, but I thought he must be a friend of yours putting on a fake Russian accent. Surely violinists don't talk on the telephone, do they?"

"I don't see why not," said Carrie, wondering what Bunin could want.

"The telephone seems too earthy for a man like Bunin. I saw him at the Albert Hall the other night, playing Mozart. . . ." Then she saw that Carrie wasn't listening, so she sipped her tea in silence.

"So how's Ben?" asked Carrie, pulling herself back to the present with an effort. "He usually enjoys the Queen's Club tournament better than Wimbledon."

"He's through the first round of the singles, but he'll be out today," said Angela, "I can't remember whom he's playing but it's someone a good deal better than he is. Do try and persuade him to give up this tennis nonsense and get a steady job. He's not even trained for anything. His father keeps persuading his friends to find openings for Ben, and he just won't listen. It's not that I object to tennis as a career if you've got the talent—you, my dear, and Jimmy, that's another matter—but Ben . . . He's been playing seriously for six years now, and most years he only just covers his expenses."

"I doubt if he'd listen to me."

The older woman smiled. "You know very well he would. If you suggested that he should give up tennis and settle down, he'd do it like a shot. He wants to marry you."

Carrie was conscious that she was under close scrutiny. She didn't want to offend Angela but at the same time she wanted to make the position clear.

"You know I'm fond of Ben, but . . ." she began, and the other woman interrupted, saying, "Don't worry, Caroline. I can guess what you're going to say.

You think of him as a brother, and you would never consider marriage."

"Something like that," Carrie admitted.

"That's all right then," said Angela, relieved. "I never thought you two were suited but it was what Ben wanted. It's almost a habit with him now, loving you. He doesn't even see other girls. You know I'm fond of you, Carrie, but you'd find Ben tedious in a week. He's just not your type. And I'd think it would be a bad idea for a man to marry someone so *much* better than he is at his chosen career."

"Are you sure you want me to stay, though?" asked Carrie, knowing that she was there at Ben's invitation.

"I'm delighted," said Angela. "You're a very easy guest—you don't talk too much, don't eat too much and you do the washing up. Besides, I'm fond of you," and she heaved her substantial body out of the sofa and gave Carrie an affectionate kiss.

Carrie was touched by Angela's attitude, but she wondered how she could manage to leave the flat for a few hours. Above all, of course, she wanted to see Nikolai. If she went to Queen's Club to see Ben—he would certainly have arranged for her to have access to the players' seats—then almost certainly Nikolai would be there.

The atmosphere at Queen's was always different from Wimbledon. It was more of a tournament, less of a social occasion, a contrast underlined by the look of the place—there were no gracious lawns or ivy-covered walls, no strawberries and cream, just wooden stands and tennis courts.

On one of these tennis courts Ben Jackson was playing. Carrie took her place next to Dallas Parfitt in the players' seats. Dallas had her head buried in her hands. "Are you okay? What's the score?" Carrie didn't even know who Ben's opponent was.

"I think he's gone crazy," said Dallas.

"Who?"

The American girl pointed to the court, and Carrie realized that Ben was playing Zanov. "It should be short and sweet, at any rate," Dallas said. According to the scoreboard Nikolai had won the first set six-love and was now leading by three games to nothing. A drastic score, but after all, Zanov was certain to win, thought Carrie, and Ben would pick up a game or two on the way. Very seldom indeed did a player of Nikolai's quality bother to win every game in an early round match when the conclusion was as foregone as this; Ben would pick up a game here and there.

But as Carrie watched, she understood Dallas's remark. It did indeed look as if Zanov had gone crazy. He was playing every point with the accuracy, tactical subtlety and devastating power appropriate to a match with Lendl or McEnroe. Ben could only do his best, which was so far from good enough that the match was a painful spectacle to watch, and the crowd, who had begun by applauding Zanov's more extravagant gets and smashes, had settled into an uneasy silence.

At one of the changeovers Dallas gripped Carrie's arm. "Why doesn't Ben claim an injury? Shall I call to him?"

"You know Ben would never do that."

"Can't you stop Zanov? It's not a match, it's a massacre. Would he stop if you asked him?" Dallas asked in her straightforward manner.

It's worth trying, thought Carrie, remembering the effort he had made for her at the match in Paris. If there was any chance at all, then it was up to her to take it. She knew Nikolai's attitude toward Ben must be on her account, and she also knew that Ben would keep playing to the last point instead of turning the match into a farce by refusing to run for the ball.

She resolved to try and catch Zanov's eye next changeover, but an even better opportunity arose. It started to rain and play was suspended. Carrie darted in to wait by the foot of the stairs to the men's changing room.

Ben was the first to appear. "Not doing very well, am I?" he said ruefully.

Carrie hugged him. "The rain looks set in for at least an hour. Change and meet me in the bar."

Next the players from the other matches streamed past her; most were silent, annoyed by the interruption of rain, but one or two greeted her and asked after her ankle. At last, when she assumed that somehow she had managed to miss Nikolai, he appeared and exclaimed at the sight of her. "I thought you were in Brighton!"

Conscious of the need for haste—Ben would reappear at any time—she stammered out her request. "Please don't give Ben such a hard time. Just beat him normally. Don't take your anger out on him."

He stood for a moment and then slammed his fist against the wall in utter frustration. They were still alone in the corridor.

"Can I help, Nikolai?" said Carrie, moved by the baffled misery in his eyes.

"There is nothing to be done," said Nikolai. "You must try and forget me."

"That's nonsense," said Carrie, but her voice was more uncertain than her words. It hurt her so much when Nikolai said things like that. "I'm staying in London," she added.

"Where?"

"At the Jacksons'."

"Will you be there for Wimbledon fortnight?"

"No, at a hotel."

A silence followed. They were standing very close together; Carrie could see a muscle twitching in Nikolai's cheek.

"Carrie . . ." he began.

Suddenly Karel Vronsky was there, his bulk filling the passageway. Carrie greeted him; with a worried smile he squeezed past her and ushered Nikolai up the stairs toward the changing room.

Carrie could have cried with disappointment. Why had Karel had to appear just then? If only Nikolai could have finished his sentence. In the present confusion any explanation or any hint of his feelings could be vital.

She trailed back to the bar despondently; waiting for Ben, she watched the raindrops trickling down the wide windows and the groundsmen struggling with vast, unwieldy tarpaulins. She felt weary. It was difficult to conduct a love affair under so many pairs of watchful eyes—Alexei and Sasha unfriendly, Karel friendly—but all intrusive.

Rain stopped play all the rest of that day; in the evening Carrie set herself to being a dutiful guest. She laughed at Philip Jackson's jokes, which wasn't difficult, as he was a good raconteur, and appreciated Angela's food, which was also not difficult. And, with Ben's company though not help, did the washing-up.

After dinner Angela insisted on watching television, and as it was a slow news day, there was some footage of the Zanov-Jackson match. Luckily neither of the Jackson parents knew enough about tennis to appreciate the finer points of Zanov's dissection of their son's play. But Ben himself was noticeably quieter after the news and soon, making his apologies to Carrie, said he'd go to bed to make sure of getting enough rest before the match the following day.

After he had gone, Philip and Angela settled down to watch the television, and Carrie, restless, set out for a walk. They protested and urged her to be careful; she agreed not to walk in the park, to stick to main roads, and soon was out in the street taking great breaths of fresh air. The Jackson flat was air-conditioned.

Soon she was walking briskly along Bayswater in the direction of Marble Arch. Nikolai was staying at Claridge's, she knew; it would do no harm to walk in that direction. It had just stopped raining and the air was warm; streetlights shimmered in the puddles, and occasionally cars swished by with a soft purring noise. She was walking by the park railings; the smell of damp grass and trees filled her nostrils, and she was happy.

As she walked through Mayfair her mind was busy with the problem of Nikolai. She understood that he was being watched. Either Sasha or Alexei, or even sometimes Vronsky, did everything they could to prevent him being alone with Carrie—perhaps did everything they could to prevent him being alone with anyone. Why this was happening she didn't know, apart from assuming that it was somehow connected with his dissident sister Sonya and the need the Russian authorities felt to prevent him escaping their influence.

And what part did Sasha play in all this? According to Pavel Bunin, Nikolai had first loved, then despised her. Nikolai himself had spoken of her in dismissive terms, but that was before she reappeared on the scene. Now, if Jimmy's information was correct, she shared hotel suites with him. She was a very beautiful woman; Carrie remembered with irksome clarity Sasha and Nikolai standing so close together at the reception in Paris, Sasha clinging to Nikolai's arm; they had appeared a team then, linked by some bond, some understanding Carrie did not share.

Carrie turned her steps away from Claridge's. She couldn't hang around outside the hotel waiting for a glimpse of Nikolai; that would look ridiculous. Neither could she walk in and demand to see him and ask him what was happening. A direct approach always appealed to her, but in this case, when she'd been given the clearest possible warning to stay away, it was out of the question.

Early next morning Carrie set herself to find Pavel Bunin's phone number. He wasn't in the phone directory, but Lady Alice was, and soon Carrie was talking to the old woman. "Yes, Pavel is staying here. He is out at the moment, but I know he wants to talk to you, and so do I."

Surprised that Lady Alice had even remembered her, Carrie arranged to go to the flat near the Albert Hall for coffee that morning.

In the daylight Lady Alice's flat was even more extraordinary; dustsheets covered most of the furniture in the rooms Carrie could glimpse as she was led to the old woman's sitting room. It was unbearably hot; despite the warm June weather a coal fire was burning in the grate, and two pug dogs snuffled and growled on cushions in front of the flames. Lady Alice, a small figure wrapped in shawls and rugs, sat in a high-backed chair drawn up to the warmth. In daylight Carrie could see just how frail and ill she looked, but the hand that shook hers still had a firm grip.

Bunin had not yet returned; Carrie was offered coffee and sweet Russian cakes. "My late husband liked these, and at first I ate them to please him. They reminded him of Russia. After eating them for forty years for his sake, I found I liked them for my own; such is the power of habit. I have never been to Russia; my husband left during the revolution, and we married shortly after."

"You have never been to Russia? But at your party you spoke Russian."

"I had to learn the language; all my husband's friends were Russian expatriates. Don't worry, my dear, you won't find it difficult."

The old lady's wandering, thought Carrie.

"Or perhaps you will not need to learn. The world has changed, and Nikolai Theodorovich speaks beautiful English; he's always been a traveler. Put more coal on the fire, then sit away from it yourself. Sit near the window, I know it is too hot in here. Tell me, is it true what Pavel says, that Nikolai is once more seen with that blond creature?"

"Do you mean Sasha White? Did you know her?"

"Only too well. When Nikolai came to London he always used to stay here, with me. His grandmother and I were girls together—and a lovely girl she was. Headstrong, self-willed, but so beautiful! Then, after she lived in Russia, we would write to each other. English letters often got lost—but when I could write in Russian, then the censor was happier, so the letters got through. We wrote to each other every month for nearly sixty years. So, when her grandson was in

London, where else would he stay if not with me? And he would bring that . . . creature with him.''

"Didn't you like her?"

"I do not like spies. That is all she was. But there was no telling Zanov. If he does not want to hear, then he doesn't hear. Until one night when they were staying here she said something to him, I don't know what, and he saw her for what she was."

"I don't understand," said Carrie. "What exactly was she?"

"An employee of the Russian government, sent to watch Nikolai. He is not a member of the Communist Party, his sister Sonya has never done what is expected of a child of the Soviet and he became internationally famous. Of course he must be watched and his attitudes to Russia understood—and who better to do this than a beautiful woman, his constant companion, the woman he loves?"

"You mean she never loved him at all?"

"With creatures like that," said the old woman with utter contempt, "who can tell if they have feelings? He was handsome, he was successful. Perhaps she loved him. Perhaps she still does."

Carrie's heart lurched.

"And now she is back," continued Lady Alice. "It worries me. Ah, here is Pavel. He also is worried, and he will tell you why."

The musician settled himself with coffee and cakes. "Miss Astell, I am very glad to see you. I hope you can help me. I have been trying to get in touch with Nikolai Theodorovich. But every time I telephone his hotel someone else answers and says he is unavailable, either a man or Sasha White."

"What can I do to help?"

"You play tennis with him, isn't that so? You must

talk to him on the court. You could give him a message."

"I could certainly do that, but not till next week. You could always write to him, of course."

"Not with any certainty that he would get the letter," said Pavel. "I have something important to tell him."

7

That afternoon Carrie went to visit the advertising firm where she used to work, partly to find out if there was any chance of a job for her in a year or so. The offices, three large rooms on the top floor of a house just off Bond Street, were, as usual, crowded with clients, photographers, secretaries, designers and copywriters, all apparently talking at once, nobody listening to anybody else. She was greeted by squeals of delight from those who knew her, which weren't many, as personnel turnover was so hectic in advertising and she had been away for two entire years.

Half an hour was long enough. Her only close friend in the firm had since left; the others struck her suddenly as empty-headed, colorful, exotic birds. She tried to feel an interest in the major new campaign they were launching for a chocolate bar. She made appropriate noises about the poster campaign, the designs for the thirty-second television film that had cost sixty thousand pounds, but her heart wasn't in it. Her boss, renowned as a charmer even in an industry that ran on charm, just seemed too carefully dressed, almost effeminate; and she realized she was comparing him with Nikolai, whose tall, muscular frame shaped her ideas of what a man should be.

Slightly shaken, Carrie walked down Bond Street. She had assumed that when she was finished with tennis, she would know what she wanted to do; now she was not at all sure—and more than that, Nikolai was taking altogether too large a place in her life. I'll think about that after Wimbledon, she told herself.

Back in Sussex on Friday the doctor gave his opinion on her ankle. "Excellent. Perfectly recovered and fit to play."

"The ankle may be fit to play, but I'm not so sure about the girl," said Tony. "Several more hours of daylight, Carrie; out onto the courts. Jimmy'll practice with you, and we'll see what disasters have befallen your game since last week."

The Wimbledon fortnight was the high point of the year for Tony Astell. Even when he hadn't coached any of the players, it was an opportunity to meet his friends, and he did interval commentaries for the BBC that gave him the chance to air his decided views on current trends in tennis. He always stayed at the same hotel in South Kensington, tucked away behind the Cromwell Road down a quiet cul-de-sac, a large double-fronted Victorian building covered with stucco like an over-iced cake, mostly inhabited by permanent residents—elderly women, often Army widows. The proprietor, Mrs. Pierce, was now over sixty but as active as ever, a devoted tennis fan who remembered the days when Tony and Betty Astell were the stars of Wimbledon. She still watched every match she could on television, and although she knew that now it was Lendl, Connors, Zanov, McEnroe, these legendary beings were less real to her than Drobny, Seixas, Hoad and Maureen Connolly.

As a small girl Carrie had stayed in the hotel with her father, enjoying the break from school, the only drawback to a blissful week being the responsibility of looking after Jimmy. Now, as she unpacked in a bedroom overlooking Cornwall Gardens and hung her clothes in the massive mahogany wardrobe, automatically counting the tennis outfits and deciding which to wear for the first day's play, she wished her problems were still so simple.

Jimmy was waiting for her in the residents' lounge, always deserted by the actual residents in favor of the television room. "You'll never guess what Tony's ordered for dinner," he said, grinning all over his face.

"Not chicken and grapefruit."

"Protein for muscles and sugar for energy," chanted Jimmy in imitation of his father. "Food for a champion."

Carrie looked around the room with its old-fashioned furniture and dusty piles of magazines— back numbers of *Country Life* and *The Lady*. "I don't want to stay here this evening," she decided. "The chicken will be tasteless and watery. You know what their cooking's like."

"I'll take you out for dinner," offered Jimmy. "To show there's no hard feelings. Your choice of restaurant."

Carrie's spirits lifted. "Good; and not a word about tennis?"

"Cross my heart and hope to die," said Jimmy. "You'll have to fix it with Tony, though."

Tony Astell was quite happy. "So long as you eat protein and vitamin C and not too much fat," he instructed earnestly. "Do you good to go out and take your mind off things. Just get back in time for eight hours sleep; we're practicing at nine thirty tomorrow, remember."

Carrie paused only to fetch a shawl.

"So where is it to be?" asked Jimmy.

"I don't in the least mind. You choose."

"I've heard of a good new place in Hampstead with French food, just off Haverstock Hill."

"Lead me to it."

"I don't think chicken in wine sauce with cream and mushrooms is quite what Tony had in mind, but it was delicious," said Carrie. "Weren't we lucky to get a table?"

The little restaurant was crowded; luckily the waiters were slim-hipped and young, because otherwise they couldn't possibly have squeezed their way between the chairs and tables. The owner, a man of about thirty with a Gallic waxed mustache, dark hair and sallow skin, talked English with such an extreme French accent that Jimmy claimed it was assumed and that he was actually from the Mile End Road.

She felt utterly carefree, all thought of tennis or Russia put away for the moment. Jimmy was at his best, his considerable energy and quick-wittedness concentrated on entertaining rather than plaguing her.

As he paid the bill and they prepared to leave, he said, "Just wait for me a minute, I've seen someone I know."

Carrie watched him cross to a table in a corner

behind her; because she wasn't expecting to see them there, it took her a few seconds to realize that the couple he was talking to was Nikolai and Sasha.

She was annoyed and angry. This was not a place where Nikolai had to be; if he'd brought Sasha out to dinner it could only be for the pleasure of her company. Mortified, her eyes stinging with unexpected tears, Carrie bent her head and concentrated on counting the checks in the tablecloth.

"Right," said Jimmy some minutes later. "I'm ready when you are."

Carrie nodded and reached under the table for her handbag. Someone passing stumbled and held her chair, apparently trying to regain his balance. It was Nikolai. Sasha, some yards nearer the door, was talking to Jimmy.

Without a word, without a look from him, Nikolai's hand grasped Carrie's and withdrew, leaving a key in her palm. Instinctively she tucked it into her handbag without looking down. When she joined Jimmy at the door, Nikolai and Sasha had gone.

In the car her mind worked furiously. A casual glance into her handbag revealed that it was a hotel room key; the address of the hotel and the number of the room were on the plastic tag. Zanov wanted her to meet him there without letting Jimmy or Sasha know about it; that much was obvious. It wasn't so clear when this meeting would be; as soon as possible was the likeliest bet, Carrie decided.

Once back at their hotel she said good night to Jimmy and went up to her room. Half an hour later, when the movements from Jimmy's room next door indicated that he was in bed, she left her room quietly and slipped downstairs. Even though it was only just eleven o'clock, the hotel was already closed for the night; she took a front door key from the shuttered reception desk and let herself out.

The address on Nikolai's key was a street in Bayswater, not far from the Jacksons' flat; as she drove through the Park she wondered if the reception clerk would let her into the hotel and up to a room if he'd never seen her before. She needn't have worried, for when she walked into the hotel, the reception clerk didn't even look up. He seemed utterly uninterested in checking the guests' comings and goings; an elderly man with glasses, he was reading a newspaper with close attention, peering at the page and moving his lips as he read.

It was a seedy hotel with no elevator, a worn staircarpet, peeling wallpaper and dusty plastic flowers stuck at random into vases. From the television room came the rattle of gunfire and the screech of tires as an American police series entered its last five minutes. As Carrie climbed the stairs she could hear the moan and gurgle of antiquated plumbing.

When she reached the correct floor she didn't even need to use her key. Nikolai flung open the door as she approached it and swept her into a crushing embrace. Finally being in his arms after the tension of the past weeks was too much; emotion flooded her and she began to cry, her whole body shuddering with sobs. Tenderly he stroked her hair, and his lips brushed her forehead. "Don't cry," he murmured.

There was so much Carrie wanted to ask him, but her anger at his treatment of her, her jealousy of Sasha and the overwhelming force of his physical presence rousing her reluctant body to immediate desire confused her. She moved away from him, determined not to let herself be drawn into anything physical.

"Tell me what's happening, Nikolai, please. Who is

Alexei? And"—her voice trembled as she hesitated to go on, dreading his answer—"who is Sasha?"

Nikolai paced restlessly round the room. "What a shabby, miserable place," he said, snapping on a bedside lamp. "Karel had to find somewhere on short notice."

"Never mind that," said Carrie. Now that Nikolai was here, she had forgotten her surroundings completely.

"Alexei works for the Russian government. His job is to keep me from staying in the West. He has to watch me at all times, stop me from making Western friends, spy on me. I have to obey his orders because otherwise it is worse for my sister. Do you understand so far?"

"And Sasha?"

"I was in love with her, once," he said, eyes dark with memory. "Until I found out what she really was. But she is also in the pay of the Russians. She and Alexei have always worked together."

"But . . ."

"At first I wanted you to think that I was with Sasha again, that we were lovers."

"Nikolai, how *could* you?" said Carrie, remembering the shock, the hurt, shrugging away the arm he put round her. "Don't, please."

"Listen to me," he said gently, putting both arms round her and preventing her from pulling away. "It is much safer for you if Alexei knows nothing about our relationship. I do not want you involved."

"Why didn't you just tell me? I could have pretended. . . ."

"That is just the point, Carrie," said Nikolai. "I do not think you could. I think you are transparently honest and genuine, and I know that Alexei can see through the pretences of much more professional deceivers than you. If he knew what I felt for you . . .''

And what is that? thought Carrie, longing for him to say something to declare himself, and confirm what her instincts told her about their relationship.

"If he knew my feelings, he would use them somehow," said Nikolai. "And it is of particular importance that he not suspect anything now."

"Why?"

"When I came to Brighton to see you, I'd just spoken to Sonya."

"You *spoke* to her? Your sister?"

"There are telephone lines to Russia, you know. She has been considering defecting to the West for some time, and she conveyed in our code that she has agreed to leave Russia."

"But why did you want her to?" Nikolai was still holding her, and Carrie looked up into his face, searching for an answer. He held her gaze steadily.

"Because I met a woman in Rome. A woman I want to be free to get to know. A woman I desired"—his voice thickened—"a woman I still desire," and his mouth moved lazily over hers.

Carrie's body longed to respond, but she was still upset, still vulnerable; too vulnerable to trust herself so close to him. Again she pulled away and this time moved beyond his reach, to the other side of the room, and stared out of the window at the blinking red neon lights of the other hotel. "Did you know that you always look out of windows, Nikolai?" she said, trying to regain control, to sort out her thoughts.

He stood beside her, a little distance away. "I hadn't noticed about the windows. Perhaps it is because I feel confined," he said. "I am looking out from my cage at all the free people, the Western people. Carrie, you must understand. I was trying to protect you from Alexei, trying to make sure Sonya has time to leave Russia before I have to return. They will take me straight back when I am eliminated from Wimbledon, but if Alexei thinks there is a real chance I will defect, he'll take me back immediately. And what could be a better reason than a woman?"

"Nikolai Zanov always has women," said Carrie, expressing one of her deepest fears, that she was only one of many.

He turned her to face him. "Look at me and tell me if you really believe that," he said. "Do you think that you are no more to me than . . . than . . ."

"Than the tennis groupie you thought I was?" she interrupted. His closeness was affecting her powerfully, and with a hesitant movement she touched his cheek. He caught her hand and kissed it.

"When we make love, is that how I treat you?" he asked. "And would you give so much to someone who cared so little?"

Carrie shook her head.

"I didn't think so," said Nikolai. "So you see, what I am hoping is that Sonya will soon be safe in Western Europe."

"And then?" said Carrie.

"And then I can stop worrying about my sister and concentrate on you," snapped Nikolai, exasperated at his situation.

"But if you don't want Alexei to know that we have a relationship, why did you meet me here tonight?"

Nikolai smiled, one eyebrow lifting in a typical, quizzical expression. "Ah. Well. That is a little difficult to explain. . . . Perhaps I had better show you." He pulled her toward him and this time there was no hesitation in her response. With a growl of passion he held her tightly and crushed her lips with his in a dominating and demanding kiss. "I have been thinking of nothing else," he muttered. "First to have you and to share what we shared, and then to watch you so hurt, to see you so proud, trying not to show that you are hurt. Carrie . . . it was painful, painful watching you with that clumsy man of yours—"

"I've told you," said Carrie. "He's not my man." She was returning his kiss and trying to talk at the same time, breathless with eagerness, luxuriating in the roughness of his stubble on her lips, on her face, inhaling the familiar, stimulating smell of him. Driven by a powerful need, she began to unbutton his shirt, longing to be closer, to feel and taste his body with her lips. His naked chest aroused her further, and she was hardly aware that he too was busy removing her blouse, her skirt. His fingers traced the lift of her breasts in the lacy white bra, then unhooked it and gripped her tightly to him.

Soon they were naked together under the worn cover of the lumpy bed. The strangeness of their surroundings momentarily chilled Carrie, and she clung to Nikolai. "I'm sorry it has to be a place like this," he said gently. His sensitivity moved her again, and she felt passion return as the warmth from his body, delightfully familiar yet still challengingly masculine, seeped into hers and his hands resumed their steady, knowledgeable caresses. He stroked her back, her shoulders, comforting and exciting her at the same time.

Tentatively at first, then growing bolder, she caressed him in return, letting his moans of pleasure guide her hands, feeling her own excitement build with his as he slipped his hand between her thighs, arousing passion she knew only he could satisfy. She wanted him completely, wanted to give herself to him completely. Her senses were swamped with the power of his lovemaking, and she clung to him with little cries of abandon, trusting him to take her to the furthest bounds of ecstasy.

It was several minutes before she returned to full awareness of their surroundings, their situation, and then it was a cruel shock. She was still firmly held in the crook of his arm, but the red neon light flashing in her eyes reminded her of the outside world. "So, what shall we do?" she asked, trusting him to know what was best. The world of circumspection and intrigue that he had to live in was strange to her.

"We will pretend not to be interested in each other," said Nikolai.

"That won't be easy for me," said Carrie.

"It's been nearly impossible for me," admitted Nikolai. "But we will try."

"Oh!" said Carrie, suddenly remembering. "Pavel Bunin asked me to ask you to telephone him."

"When did you see him?"

"This morning. At Lady Alice's. We ate Russian cakes and chatted; it was the nicest thing that's happened to me for days. Until this evening, of course," she added as he looked at her in mock reproach, and settled herself in his arms again. "How long can you stay, Nikolai?"

"Another two hours," he said.

"That's lucky; so can I," said Carrie nonchalantly. "I wonder what we'll find to do?"

Next morning, after a deep sleep, the most relaxed she had had since Sasha appeared on the scene, Carrie went down to breakfast and found Tony in a state of tension.

"You were out last night! I went into your room at one o'clock, and you weren't there." Carrie began to give some invented explanation, but Tony cut her short. "Carrie, I don't mind where you were; it's your life and I don't interfere, you know that. But your sleep, your rest—how are you going to play? How am I to keep you in training?"

Carrie patted her father's hand soothingly. He was always like this when significant matches were on the horizon; he had set his heart on her doing well in this tournament. "Stop fussing. I'm not playing a match until tomorrow; I'm very fit, thanks to your training program—and diet," she added hastily, "and I feel perfectly rested."

"You look all right," he admitted. "Any trouble with the ankle?"

"None at all."

"Right. We'll leave in half an hour."

It was an unreal morning for Carrie. Normally the first morning of the first day of Wimbledon was a very special time. All the old regulars would greet each other; the players, some sociable, some silent, would be preparing for their matches that afternoon. The good-humored noise of the crowds lining up outside could be heard while the still-inexperienced food vendors dashed around with trays of edibles looking self-important. The little groups of grim-faced men with cables, television equipment, microphones and cameras would shout incomprehensible things to each other as the final adjustments were made to the great camera crane towering over the center court. The groundsmen would either be admiring the state of the courts or making dire prognostications about the weather. All of these things normally added up to the beginning of the tremendous atmosphere building up to finals that made it the greatest tournament in the world. Usually Carrie enjoyed every moment, every meeting; she didn't suffer from match nerves until just before she was due to play; but this morning going through her strokes under Tony's demanding eye, she was preoccupied with Nikolai. In one way her mind was now set at rest; she was absolutely convinced that she was very important to him. She no longer had any fears concerning his relationship with Sasha. But at the same time she was convinced that he was determined to protect her, Carrie, from any involvement with him that might prove damaging for her. He certainly wasn't prepared to let her return to Russia with him.

She weighed the possibilities. If he had to return to Russia, then she could go too—even without his permission. It must be possible to visit Moscow as a tourist, she thought, and when I'm there, perhaps he'll see things differently.

"Concentrate, Carrie! I said we'd work on your backhand drive now. Backhand!" Tony called impatiently.

"Yes, sorry," said Carrie. "I was miles away."

"Half an hour more and then you can have lunch."

"I'll go for a walk instead. I want to be alone for a while."

There was no need for Carrie to go back to Wimbledon that afternoon; her father was finished with her for the day. After two o'clock, when play started, no courts would be available for practice so early in the tournament as this. She told herself that she was going to watch the center court match between McEnroe, always an exciting player, and one of Ben's friends, a cheerful young Australian. The

Australian might even get a set or two; he was improving by leaps and bounds. It should be a good match, thought Carrie, all the time conscious that her real interest was the second match on court five between N. Zanov (USSR) and A. Patel (I). Patel wouldn't win, unless something went badly wrong; almost a veteran now, the Indian at his best had been an elegant player with some of the best touch strokes in tennis, but nothing to stand up to Zanov's power-house serve and volley game.

As she approached the front gates one of a group of schoolgirls recognized her, and she was surrounded by eager autograph-hunters. The young nun in charge of the party vainly tried to control them, but Carrie laughed off her apologies, busy signing. "Don't worry, I'm glad to do it. I used to wait in line for autographs myself at their age."

"Good luck! Good luck!" the girls called out to her as she left. It was a heartening little encounter, and not even the sight of Alexei hovering near the center court could spoil her good mood. She decided to disconcert him by a direct approach.

"Hello, Alexei. You look cross."

"It is bedlam," he said simply. "I did not expect this."

"Didn't expect what?"

He waved his hand to indicate the passing crowds, the policemen, the officials. "Everyone just walks about. Wherever they like. The players have to walk among the crowds to get to outside courts—anyone can just run up and talk to them."

"It's always been like that."

"It is not so in my country. How can I protect Nikolai?"

Protect was presumably a euphemism for "watch,"

but Carrie pretended to take him seriously. "What are you going to protect him from? I seem to remember he had men in raincoats to protect him in Rome."

"That was from the crowd. A Roman crowd can be dangerous to an unpopular player. You know that. But England is supposedly safe."

"I don't think a player's ever been injured by the crowd at Wimbledon," laughed Carrie. "Don't worry."

She walked past him in search of her father, found him and made sure he wouldn't tell Jimmy about her nocturnal escapade. He was chatting to Paula Krantz, who tactfully moved away so father and daughter could speak privately. "Join us," she invited when Carrie had finished. "We were just talking about publicity. How's the romance with Zanov going? It's a good angle for the press, especially as you're a mixed-doubles team."

"I don't *have* a romance with Zanov," said Carrie, very conscious that Nikolai had asked her to keep her distance. "I usually go about with—with Ben Jackson," she went on. That should put Paula off the scent, she thought. Her father looked astounded, and she kicked him in the ankle. "Don't I, Tony? I was staying with the Jacksons only last week."

Paula's sharp eyes moved from father to daughter and back again. She was suspicious, Carrie could see. "Ben Jackson's a steady young player," she said, "and a good-looking boy. He's not the player Zanov is, of course."

"I think Zanov has a chance of winning this year," said Tony. "I was just talking to Dan Maskell about it."

"You think he has a chance against McEnroe?" Fortunately Paula's interest had been diverted. "And he'll have to play Lendl first—he's in the same half of the draw."

"Excuse me," said Carrie, and slipped away to court five. As she moved through the crowds she could see Alexei's point. Internationally famous athletes moved through a swirling mass of people protected only by an assortment of line judges and officials.

"Carrie! Good!" said Ben from behind her. "I thought I saw you."

"Why aren't you watching the center court match? You should be giving loyal support."

"It's over. John wrapped it up in three sets. Come and have tea with me."

"There's a long line."

"I can fix that—I know one of the girls serving."

There was no way out; Carrie could see Paula Krantz watching them. With as good grace as she could muster, she went to have tea with Ben, and as the assistant serving was a fan of his, Carrie enjoyed the pick of the cakes without having to wait.

Time dragged by. Carrie kept glancing surreptitiously at her watch. At last she said casually, "Who's on number seven?"

"I can't remember. A pair of Americans, I think; not a seed, anyway."

"Could it be them?" She indicated two exhausted-looking players trailing back to the changing room.

"Those are Americans all right. I beat one of them in Rome. What's your interest in it?"

"Patel is playing next on seven; you know how I admire his game," said Carrie at random.

"Do you?" said Ben. "I always think he should have been a squash player with those peculiar fiddly little shots. Here he comes, anyway. Poor chap, he's playing Zanov; I feel for him. Do you suppose that blond man with Zanov is a bodyguard?"

The group did look odd as it advanced toward them. Patel, a small skinny man with a high-pitched voice, was talking excitably to a silent Nikolai. Alexei, equally silent, strode immediately behind Zanov, wearing a raincoat despite the heat; next to him waddled Karel, carrying rackets and towels.

Carrie, remembering Nikolai's warnings not to show an interest in him, tried not to catch his eye; she went on talking to Ben without looking up.

"I tell you what," said Ben, "I'll come with you. You're right, it should be an interesting match; they're both tacticians, and I could learn a lot from that. My tactics are primitive."

"When's your match?"

"Third on court twelve; officially not due to start till six, but it'll be later. I've plenty of time. Come on or we'll miss the beginning of Patel and Zanov."

So Carrie watched the match in Ben's company; at least this way it doesn't look as if I'm after Nikolai, she thought, and was even more relieved to have company when Sasha appeared. The other woman, dressed flamboyantly and flatteringly in a white silk suit, settled herself next to Alexei in the row behind Carrie and applauded loudly whenever the Russian won a point.

Zanov was playing very well; his strokes were elegant, apparently effortless and graceful, yet remorselessly effective—so like the man himself. Carrie lost all trace of doubt about their future as she watched. Such a man must succeed in getting what he wants, she thought, even if his opponent is Soviet Russia. Then she returned to reality. After all, tennis was only a game, and perhaps her romantic belief that everything would turn out well for them was only a dream.

After dinner that night Tony was watching the news and weather in the square, dimly lit, unprepossessing television room of his hotel, surrounded by elderly women who regarded him with hostility and suspicion as not only a stranger but a strange man.

"Carrie, Carrie!" he called as she passed the door. "It's going to rain tomorrow, according to the weather forecast."

"Shhh," said three old ladies.

"Don't trust the weathermen; you know how often they're wrong," said Carrie quietly, coming to sit beside him.

"But I've just remembered, we haven't done tactics for you."

"If the match is interrupted, you can tell me what to do while we're waiting for play to resume. I'm going to bed, anyway. I want a long, restful bath."

"Not too long, and not too hot. Baths can be enervating."

"Shhh," said the three old ladies again.

"You'll be lucky if there's any hot water," added a fourth.

"Why don't you hire a television?" Carrie whispered in his ear. "Then you could watch the tennis in your room."

"Good idea." He followed her out to the hall. "How are you feeling? Ankle still sound?"

"Perfectly." Carrie wondered what he wanted to say; he moved from foot to foot awkwardly and rubbed his hands together. "About tomorrow," he finally managed.

"What about it?"

"I just wanted to say . . . it doesn't matter if you lose."

"I know it doesn't," said Carrie. "You've always said that, and I've always believed it."

"I just thought—what with me going on and on about Wimbledon—that you might think I'd be disappointed if you lost."

"You would be."

"Not especially," lied Tony valiantly. "It's only a tournament, after all."

Carrie kissed his cheek. "Good night, then."

"One more thing; it's been worrying me rather. What you said to Paula about going round with Ben—you're not serious, are you?"

"Promise you won't tell Paula? No, I'm not."

"Oh, good."

"I thought you liked Ben."

"I do. He's a nice enough chap."

"But?"

"You need someone with more go to him. Like your Russian, for instance. Besides, even more important— Ben's such a rotten tennis player."

It was raining next morning; heavy, gray, unremitting English rain swept by gusts of wind. "It looks set in to me," said Tony, drawing the curtains back as Carrie blinked into wakefulness. "Here's some papers and your post; mostly good-luck cards forwarded from Brighton. And something from Ben."

"What time is it?"

"Eight thirty. Want some tea?"

"No, thanks."

Left alone, Carrie shuffled through her good-luck cards to read any from special friends, and finally opened the one from Betty Astell. It was characteristically matter-of-fact. "Hope all goes well for you. If you get to the center court, remember to curtsey to the royal box. Don't let Zanov hog the net. He can cover the baseline. Love, Betty."

Next, she turned to the newspapers. Tony had already been through them and marked any mention of Carrie; the *Telegraph* even ran a featured article and a photograph captioned "The golden girl of British tennis." Not bothering to read the article, Carrie looked through the foreign news section to see if there was any more information about Sonya, but there wasn't.

In the course of the morning the rain stopped. "You'll be playing on very soggy grass," said Tony gloomily; the tournament car, crawling along in a line of traffic over Putney Bridge, lurched to a halt.

"Sorry about this," said the woman driver, "there's construction just ahead. We'll be moving soon."

Tony looked at his watch again. "You won't have long to warm up," he worried. "Make sure you take no risks during the game. Any skids on that ankle of yours, and you'll be out of the tournament."

Carrie agreed, smiled, nodded, and paid no attention. She was concentrating on clearing her mind of everything except tennis and her own preparation for an important match. She knew too much time, too much emotion, had been spent in the last few days for her to be approaching the tournament in peak condition; she thought of Betty's hopes for her, Tony's ambition.

Then all too soon the intervening time was over and she found herself walking toward court fifteen, Tony giving last-minute advice, on her right her opponent, a tall Italian girl, choking back tears from nerves. Several photographers clustered round her as they reached the court, and Carrie smiled obligingly to the right, to the left, straight ahead, hoping wryly that the photographs wouldn't appear in the papers the next day beside accounts of her courageous first-round defeat. But she'd played Maria Calgari twice before and had not yet had trouble beating her. That afternoon the Italian girl seemed set on her own destruction. Nerves made her tense; she ran for balls she should have left, skidded on the slippery ground, and soon her long legs and once-white shorts were covered in mud and grass stains, which annoyed her further. Carrie won the first set six-two, and then the Italian disputed a decision of the line judge, burst into tears and from then on her game disintegrated completely.

"One down, one to go," said Tony exultantly, leading her away after the photographers and autograph hunters had finished. "Your mixed doubles match will probably start on time—court four is running ahead; they've had a cancelation. No sign of Zanov yet."

"There's over an hour to go. He'll turn up," said Carrie, looking forward to his company, to the match, elated by her victory.

"When you change for the mixed doubles, put on that dress I like—the one with the pink lining to the skirt and pink piping on the bodice—that you wore in the Italian Open."

"I didn't know you were superstitious," said Carrie, amused.

"Not likely. Paula's laying on American journalists for some publicity about the new contract, and she wants you and Zanov together."

"He's not going to like that at all."

"He usually likes publicity," said Tony, his stubbornness revealing a slight doubt.

"Remember Rome? He was angry about that."

"He never said so to me."

"I'm sure he won't like it." Carrie was in a difficult position. She couldn't explain to her father without letting him know more about Zanov's affairs than the Russian would like. "It'll be all right, I expect, so long as Paula hasn't hinted about a romance between us. That'll annoy Sasha." This, a reasonably plausible explanation, satisfied Tony, and he promised to try and convince Paula, although both father and daughter were aware that the American woman tended to go her own way once she had made up her mind.

The changing room was full; apart from the one or two uncommunicative players who sat in corners concentrating on their mental readiness for a coming match and the returning losers who tended to cry or slam their rackets about, it was a cheerful, noisy place, and Carrie had to undergo a good deal of good-natured teasing about the wildly optimistic assessments the British press were making about her prospects in the tournament. Gradually the room emptied as the three o'clock competitors headed for the waiting room, and she was left drying her hair in comparative peace. Elaborate hairstyles were out of place on court, so she usually tied her hair back, but today with the cold weather she decided to let it hang loose to her shoulders. Tony, waiting for her outside, whistled as she emerged. "Clever girl! You look beautiful—Paula'll be delighted. Still no sign of Zanov. The officials say he's coming under his own steam without a tournament car, and I rang his hotel to check that he'd left."

"What did they say?"

"No answer from his suite."

"Then he's probably on his way. How long have we got?"

"Ten minutes."

"No sign of Karel or Alexei either?"

"No."

Several people were already in the waiting room, including their opponents; the American man was a good singles player of the middle rank who was beginning to ease into doubles as his thirties approached, and his new partner was a ferocious Czech with one of the strongest serves in women's tennis. This was the first time they'd played a match together, and Carrie had no idea how the partnership would jell. She was far more anxious about this match than her singles; if she and Zanov were put out of the doubles so soon, she would probably have no further opportunity to talk to him.

The hands of the clock ticked forward; the room was in silence. Outside were roars of appreciation and applause from the center court crowd as Hana Mandlikova finished off her first-round opponent.

The door opened. "If you're ready," said their official, "Miss Villefour and Miss Wade for court one."

"Where the devil is he?" said Tony. "I'll go along to the changing room."

The door opened again. "Court four, please, mixed doubles." The official looked round the room. "Is Mr. Zanov not here?" There was a miserable pause.

"He'll be changing," said the American good-naturedly. "The traffic's real bad today. Give it a minute or two."

"Here," said Zanov, bursting into the room, still pulling on his shirt. "Sorry to keep you."

"Not at all," said the official, bemused by this

politeness from a player who might just as well have started complaining about the Wimbledon clocks being wrong.

"How's the golden girl of British tennis?" said Zanov as he and Carrie sorted out their equipment by the umpire's chair.

"The English press say that about absolutely anyone," said Carrie. "Especially if they have blond hair."

"Aren't you going to ask what kept me?"

"Aren't you going to ask how I did against Maria Calgari?"

"You won."

"Who told you?"

"Nobody needed to."

Zanov was in good spirits, and Carrie wondered if he had received news through Pavel Bunin. She decided to risk asking; the Czech girl was still in earnest consultation with her partner about what racket to use in the humid conditions.

"How's Sonya? Did Pavel tell you anything?"

Nikolai grimaced. "He pointed out to me a little item in the *Times* yesterday. According to a Russian news agency, Sonya is under house arrest in Moscow."

"But you don't believe it?"

"Only a little. A niggling little doubt. But it is quite usual to give misleading information through the official agencies. Pavel is still hopeful, and he is in touch with people who know."

Their opponents were on court, waiting. There was no chance of conversation until they changed ends after the first game. "So you still expect Sonya to leave the Soviet Union soon?"

"Any day now."

Neither Carrie nor Nikolai were on form for the first set, and they lost it five-seven. During one of the breaks Carrie looked at the players' seats; Tony was grinning at her encouragingly, and she felt remorseful. She was playing without concentration or effort, because she was so happy to be with Nikolai, so happy to feel confident in their relationship, whatever else happened.

Nikolai noticed her expression.

"Something wrong?"

"I'm not concentrating."

"Neither am I."

"I'd noticed," said Carrie, lightheartedness banishing her momentary concern. "You're supposed to be the great tennis player, remember? Too many unforced errors in that last game." She was teasing him, secure in the knowledge that he would not respond in any way that Alexei could see and draw conclusions from.

"You just wait," he said quietly, his eyes wicked with promise. "Wait till we're alone, and then we'll discuss my unforced errors."

"On court, please," said the umpire, and they returned to the match. Although neither returned to full concentration, their opponents began to tire, and the sheer range of Nikolai's strokes began to tell.

"Game, set and match to Mr. Zanov and Miss Astell," said the umpire just as it started to rain again, and Carrie remembered Paula's reporters only when they surrounded her and Nikolai, with Paula in tow.

"Come on now, you two, give us a kiss for the cameras," said Paula.

Zanov looked at her blankly. "Give us a kiss," she repeated, and the Russian solemnly took Paula in his arms and gave her a smacking kiss; while she was still recovering, he disappeared in the direction of the changing rooms, and a flustered Paula was left with Carrie.

"What are *you* laughing at?" demanded Paula.

Carrie, delighted at Nikolai's skillful maneuver, struggled to compose herself.

"I guess his English isn't too good," said Paula thoughtfully. "I meant him to kiss *you*. Never mind, there she is, boys."

Carrie stood patiently answering questions and smiling. Yes, she was pleased to have won. No, she had no idea what her chances were in the singles. Yes, Wimbledon was a great tournament. Yes, her father was her only coach. Yes, she was delighted that Paula would manage her affairs in America. Yes, America was the tennis center of the world. No, she had no marriage plans at the moment. Yes, she was very lucky to have Nikolai Zanov as a doubles partner.

At last Paula clapped her hands with much jangling of bracelets. "We don't want this lovely young girl catching cold, do we?" she said, and Carrie was left in comparative peace to put on her track suit.

"You were quite charming, my dear," said Paula, walking back with her. "Pity Nikolai misunderstood me."

Waiting for her at the hotel, Carrie found a note from Pavel Bunin enclosing two tickets for a concert he was giving that night at the Festival Hall. "Please see me afterward if you are able to come," said the scrawly, foreign-looking writing. Carrie made her way to the South Bank by underground. The mundane demands of public transport were a welcome contrast to her usual pampered tennis-player's life. She was tired of the press, tired of photographs and being on show. Casually dressed in faded jeans and a sweat shirt, a thick aran sweater thrown over her shoulders to wear in case the evening turned cold or the rain restarted, she ran up the escalator at Waterloo two at a time, feeling liberated. She got to her seat early and read the program, then looked round her as the hall gradually filled up and the orchestra began tuning up. The empty seat beside her was soon the only one as far as she could see, and she remembered the last concert of Bunin's, in Nikolai's company. What would Nikolai do with the rest of his life? Surely it would be impossible always to work at one thing, tennis, when your great passion was for another, music? And surely it would be impossible even to play tennis under the present pressure?

Mozart's music filled the hall, and she abandoned thought for the patterns of glorious sound.

8

Carrie went to see Pavel Bunin in his dressing room after the concert. "I'm glad you enjoyed it," he said, paying no attention to the appreciative cries and kisses showered on him by excitable Russian friends. "Please, will you wait for me? Come back to Alice's flat and have a drink. I must consult you."

"What about?"

"Tennis," said Bunin.

Carrie was still trying to make sense of his words when they finally settled down in Lady Alice's drawing room with pug dogs snuffling round them and Alice herself pouring them Champagne. "I'll tell you our problem," he explained. "I've been in touch with friends of Sonya. They are trying to arrange her departure from Russia."

Carrie nodded.

"But they need more information about the time

145

scale involved. I sent them these, but they didn't help."

He handed her a sheaf of papers and she shuffled through them. "These are the Wimbledon playing schedules."

"I want your opinion on when Nikolai Theodorovich will be eliminated."

"From which competition? He's in three."

"Her friends need an estimate of the earliest likely date for Zanov to be out of the tournament altogether."

"The earliest *possible* date is the day after tomorrow. But the earliest *likely* date—that's anybody's guess. It's very hard to predict, Pavel."

"You play with him, you know his state of mind, you know all the circuit gossip," said Bunin firmly. "I would trust your judgment."

"It'll take some time. When do you want it?"

"Tonight," said Bunin. "If it can be done."

Forty minutes later she pushed the papers back to him. "There you are. I've marked almost certain victories with an asterisk, making my own judgments on how the other matches in his half of the draw will go. When the asterisks stop, he's out."

Bunin studied her marks. "You say he'll be out of the singles by the end of the first week. He's a top tennis player—shouldn't he at least reach the last sixteen?"

"Look at the draw. I've marked who I think he'll have to play, and they're both hard hitters with good temperaments who fight for every point. If his concentration isn't one hundred percent, either of them could beat him."

"And you think he might be out of the men's doubles on Friday?"

"Easily."

"That doesn't give Sonya very long."

"There's the mixed doubles. Look at my prediction for that. Wednesday of the final week."

"You hope to reach the semifinal?"

"Yes. It's a much more scratch event, the mixed doubles—not much money in it; it's fun, and the crowd enjoys it. Our opponents aren't great in the early rounds. I think we should do it."

"Wednesday next week might be possible," he mused. "I hope you are right."

"Should I tell Nikolai about this?"

"I'll be in touch with him soon. I'll speak to him about this."

"I'm feeling lucky today," said Dallas, stepping out of the shower.

"I've always meant to ask you, why do you shower *before* we play?"

"Wouldn't want to be anything less than sparkling clean for the British crowd, would I? Especially when my partner's the Hope of British Tennis." Carrie made a face at her. "Hey," Dallas went on, "that reminds me, did you see the great photograph in the *Times* this morning? Zanov kissing Paula Krantz? Why did he do that, d'you know?"

"I never know what Zanov's going to do," said Carrie.

"Paula looked real surprised," said Dallas. "It was funny. How long've we got?"

"Fifteen minutes."

"Okay, I'll strap my ankle; then I'm ready."

It was a perfect June day, blue sky dotted with little puffs of cloud, a slight breeze to keep the temperature down just enough to make playing comfortable. The match was on one of the open-admission outside courts; the friendly crowd greeted Carrie with enthusiastic cheers and joking advice. The grass underfoot, dried by the breeze, was springy and firm. We're going to lose, thought Carrie as she served the first ball of the match. Everything's too perfect; even Dallas feels lucky, and that's always a bad sign.

It took their opponents under an hour to beat them. Dallas was serving erratically; at crucial moments she double-faulted, and this annoyed her enough to throw off her judgment for the rest of the match. She tried to take shots that should have been Carrie's, then left shots that should have been hers. She trailed back to the changing rooms crestfallen and guilty. "That was all my fault," she said. "I'm real sorry."

"Forget it," said Carrie. "I wasn't playing my best either. It happens. They'll probably go on to win the final; then you'll feel better."

"Lucky I got a bye in the first round of the singles," muttered Dallas. "Oh, Dad," she said as her redoubtable father and coach appeared, "what happened?"

"You played like a Kentucky mule, that's what happened," said Herb Parfitt. "I just apologized to Tony Astell here for you spoiling his little girl's chances."

"I've told Herb not to give it a thought," said Tony. "Many's the match Dallas has saved for you."

"True," said Carrie, exhausted. All the hard work and strain of the past few days was beginning to catch up with her. "If you don't mind," she said to Tony, "I'll go straight back to the hotel and to bed."

"Nothing wrong with you?"

"Just tired." She changed and the tournament car took her back; within five minutes of reaching the hotel she was asleep.

Hours later—how many hours she did not at first realize, being too sleepy to read the clock—the telephone rang. "Miss Astell, this is Reception. We have a message for you. Mr. Zanov called; he wants you to meet him this evening. Nine o'clock, and he said you'd know where."

Carrie, now fully awake, saw that it was nearly eight. If Zanov didn't specify a meeting place, he could only mean the seedy hotel in Bayswater where they had met the other night. Unless he meant Alice's flat near the Albert Hall. If it was Alice's flat, then she must know about it; Carrie tried a telephone call to the old lady, who was perfectly amiable and chatted about this and that without mentioning a visit from Carrie later that evening.

So it must be the hotel. Carrie bathed and dressed, said a few words to her father, choked down the plateful of steamed chicken and broccoli the kitchens were keeping warm for her, and set out into the London night. Her car was still parked where Jimmy had left it the night before; turning the ignition on, she noticed the tank was nearly empty and drove slowly looking for an open garage.

The attendant was a tennis fan who wouldn't stop talking. He had strong opinions and welcomed the chance to air them; Carrie couldn't interrupt him without being rude, but the hands of her watch were creeping onward, and she couldn't possibly be at the hotel by nine now.

It was a quarter past as she drew up. There was no time to look for a parking place, so she left the car where it was and ran inside, seized by an irrational, desperate conviction that Nikolai would already have left.

The reception clerk was still absorbed in his newspaper. "Anyone booked here by the name of Zanov?" He shook his head. "Astell? Vronsky?"

"Make up your mind, miss." He peered at her with red-rimmed, watery eyes. "Don't I know you?"

"I came here last Sunday. Room Fourteen. Let me look at your records, please; then I'll know what name the room was booked under. It'll probably be the same tonight."

The clerk looked at her reproachfully. "Now then, young lady, what kind of hotel do you think this is? People booking in under assumed names? This is a respectable place. You can't look at the records. The very idea! Do you want a room or not?"

Carrie steadied herself. Shouting at the man would do no good, though she longed to. "I'm sorry," she apologized. "I didn't mean to criticize the hotel or your management of it."

"I'm not the manager; I'm the reception clerk."

"But it's important that I meet my friend. He might be here already; a very tall man, brown hair and eyes, probably wearing a dark suit. Has anyone like that come in within the last hour or two?"

"And if they had, what makes you think I'd tell you?"

Carrie pressed money into his hand. "I know your time is valuable."

He softened a little. "That's a better way to go about it, young lady. No. I haven't seen anyone like your friend this evening. We don't often get men in suits around here."

He must have been delayed, thought Carrie. "Then I'd like to book a room please, a double room."

"What name would that be?" said the old clerk.

Better keep Zanov out of this, thought Carrie. "Astell's the name."

"Mr. and Mrs. Astell, would that be?"

"No. I don't know what name he'll give, but if he asks for me, please send him up to my room."

"That'll be twenty-five pounds. In advance."

Carrie paid, took the key and went upstairs past the television room, where from the screech of wheels and gunfire she gathered that another American police series was in progress. Now that she was near to seeing Nikolai, she felt so happy that even the seedy familiarity of the hotel appealed to her. She wasn't in the same room as before, but she might as well have been; it was furnished with equal lack of taste, but instead of being lit by a flashing red neon sign, there was a sickly green light from the hotel's own name fastened just over the window.

She didn't have so long to wait this time. No more than five minutes later a key scratched in the lock, and she moved toward the door eagerly.

"Good evening, Carrie," said Alexei Peters, closing the door behind him. "What a pleasant surprise."

Carrie's heart gave a lurch, and her pulse began to race. It was a trap, and she had fallen for it. Presumably Nikolai had never called at all—only Alexei, to confirm what Sasha had failed to find out, that Carrie and Nikolai had indeed met in secret.

"Good evening, Alexei."

The Russian took off his white raincoat and tossed it casually on a chair. "You're going to ask me to stay, I hope."

"Hardly. I'm not going to be here long myself."

He looked at her in the way she had come to hate, his ice-chip eyes moving very slowly up and down her body. It was all she could do not to shrink away from him, and she pulled her shawl closer round her shoulders.

"I think you're frightened of me," he said conversationally. "Don't be. If you are honest, there is nothing to be frightened of. I know and you know that you came here to meet Zanov. Unfortunately Nikolai is otherwise engaged. He could not be here, so I am here instead."

As he spoke he moved toward her; Carrie moved away as casually as she could, noticing that he always kept between her and the door.

"Do stand still," he said. "You are making me dizzy, moving about like that."

"I want you to leave," said Carrie as coolly as she could manage.

He laughed. "As to that, you must have learned by now that we can't always get what we want in this world. Tell me how often you and Zanov have met."

"We haven't," said Carrie unblinkingly.

"You met a man here, last Sunday. The clerk at the desk told me."

"Not Nikolai," said Carrie.

"Who then?"

"It's none of your business," said Carrie, and she continued to deny meeting Nikolai firmly and repetitively until Alexei's attention wavered for an instant, and with split-second reflexes, Carrie dove for the door. Alexei's body slammed into her, and the side of her face hit the door frame, but Carrie hardly noticed the pain as she tore down the steps. She heard Alexei stumble behind her and she managed to reach her car well ahead of him, thanking her stars she'd parked it so close.

"Carrie!" said Tony Astell, appalled. "What in the world happened to you?" She struggled awake, blinking into the sudden light from the drawn curtains.

"What do you mean?" she stalled, remembering Alexei and the night before, wondering what her face looked like and what explanation she could get away with.

"Your face! It's all swollen! Do you feel ill?"

"No," she said, getting out of bed and looking at herself in the mirror. One side of her face was badly swollen and bruised, but she wasn't cut, and there was no trace of a black eye. "I hit my head on—on a car door. I shut it too quickly."

Tony tut-tutted, inspecting the injury closely. "You were very lucky; it could have hit your eye. Is your head painful?"

"My cheek throbs, but that's all."

"Vision fuzzy? Balance affected? Any nausea?"

"No." She wished he would go away and leave her to think. "Can I have scrambled eggs for breakfast?" She knew that request would send him in search of them, though the thought of eating made her feel sick. Sure enough, he bustled away, and she was left alone looking at her battered face in the dressing-table mirror.

Step by step she went through the scene with Alexei. She hadn't admitted meeting Nikolai—poor comfort, since Alexei knew that well enough from the desk clerk. The real damage was that he now must be convinced that Nikolai and Carrie were closely involved, and therefore be even more certain that Nikolai had reasons to defect. Nikolai will be bundled back to Russia just as soon as he's out of this tournament, she thought.

All the more necessary to make sure that they reached the mixed doubles semifinal, as Carrie had so blithely predicted to Pavel Bunin. There were three more matches to play before then. That very afternoon she and Nikolai had to play a second-round match, and she had a singles game to play immediately before. Not *immediately* before—there's the usual hour's break, she reminded herself, though she knew only too well how short an hour can be to recover if you're completely exhausted.

She looked at herself in the mirror again. Paula Krantz is going to be just furious as well, she thought. No good publicity photographs of Carrie Astell for a day or two. But the brief amusement Carrie felt from this reflection died away in moments as thoughts of Nikolai returned. What a fool I was, thought Carrie.

She dressed and went downstairs. "You're not going anywhere till you've eaten your breakfast," insisted Tony. "And then, wherever you want to go, I'll drive you." His mind was made up; she could tell from the stubborn set of his jaw. "You're not fit to be out alone, and that's the truth."

"What do you mean?"

"Shutting a car door on your face indeed. What kind of a thing is that to do right in the middle of the Wimbledon fortnight?"

"But . . ."

"Don't argue."

"Right," said Carrie. "I've arranged to go to Angela Jackson's to pick up some clothes I left there."

"How lovely to see you both," said Angela blithely. "Carrie, you poor dear, try raw steak or cold tea bags on that face. Why don't you tell Ben you're here. He's in his room doing weight-training."

Leaving Tony with Angela in the kitchen, Carrie joined Ben. She sat down on the bed and tucked her feet underneath her, leaving him floor space for exercising; then to her own amazement she began to cry, the tears spilling from her eyes faster than her trembling fingers could wipe them away. He put his arms round her. At first he was comforting; then her longing for Nikolai made Ben's presence no more than a reminder of his absence.

"What happened to your face?" he demanded.

"A car door hit me."

"You'll have to do better than that."

Carrie poured out a garbled account of the previous evening; when she finished, he gave a long sigh. "You're in love with that Russian," he said flatly. "Why doesn't he take better care of you?"

Carrie shook her head miserably.

"If he can't, then I will," Ben continued, his face unwontedly grim. He started to fling clothes into a nylon duffel bag. "Give me a hand with this lot, there's a girl. Count the shorts and shirts as they go in."

"Why are you packing?"

"I told you, I'm going to look after you. I'll stay in Jimmy's room at your hotel. Next time anyone wants to amuse themselves by beating you up, we'll see how they like discussing it with someone their own size." Carrie, relieved at the thought of his protection, protested half-heartedly: "Alexei didn't beat me up, I told you. I just hit the door when I was leaving."

"Because you were running away," said Ben. "And he was chasing you."

Carrie wasn't even sure why she was so upset. It was partly the utter lack of emotion in Alexei. He appeared outside of normal human concerns.

Angela appeared in the doorway. "Coffee, anyone?"

"I'm going to stay with Jimmy for a week or two," said Ben.

"Oh," said Angela with a knowing glance at Carrie's face. "That'll be nice; you can make sure she doesn't walk into any more doors."

By the middle of the afternoon Carrie was very tired of knowing glances. Her account of her accident was greeted with hoots of derision in the changing rooms; to her own relief, as the morning passed fear had gradually given way to exasperation, and once her singles match began, there was no time to think of anything except tennis. She was playing on court one; the capacity crowd was enthusiastic, and Carrie struggled to deserve their support. Her Australian opponent, a magical but uneven player with a temperament so relaxed as to be almost indifferent to success or failure, won a hard-fought first set, lost the second set with disconcerting suddenness and, recovering form, took the third set to a tie-break finish, which Carrie finally won.

"Game, set and match to Miss Astell." Carrie thanked the umpire, waved to the crowd, tried to smile for the photographers, dreading what she must look like. In an hour's time she would be walking out on court once more, this time with Zanov. Her singles match had been a punishing one, but Nikolai at least would be fresh.

"Come on, then," said Ben, taking her rackets. "Muscles Jackson at your disposal. Back for a rest and some glucose tablets, Tony says." Carrie didn't ask how his doubles match had gone; his glum face told the story.

The waiting room was crowded when Carrie entered with Ben, who insisted on staying as close to her as possible; three mixed-doubles games were due on court in the next few minutes. Nikolai was leaning against the far wall, listening impassively while Karel

Vronsky gabbled at him in Russian, and watching the door. His face lit up when Carrie came in, and he moved toward her; then he saw Ben and leaned back against the wall again.

Not till they were on court was there a chance to speak without being overheard. Carrie could see Alexei and Sasha sitting together in the front row of the players' enclosure. Even at thirty yards distance Alexei frightened her, and she shivered.

Zanov took her arm in an apparently casual gesture that sent thrills through her entire body; she longed for privacy, to tell him about Alexei, to hold him and be comforted.

"Tell me how you were hurt," said Nikolai. Carrie explained.

"It was a dreadful mistake," she concluded. "I should have listened to your warning."

"It *was* a mistake," said Zanov, "but not yours. He was likely to find out we'd met. It was a risk I took."

"Mr. Zanov and Miss Astell, on court, please." The umpire tapped his pencil impatiently. "We're all waiting for you."

Any doubts Carrie had felt that morning about winning the mixed doubles match were rapidly dissipated. Nikolai, playing at the top of his form, systematically annihilated their opponents. Even before the umpire called the final point, he was heading off court. "Take care, and keep away from Alexei," he said as he passed Carrie, and he gave her arm a reassuring squeeze. He was striding purposefully, quickly, and Carrie was anxious. Perhaps he was going to make trouble with Alexei; then it would be even more her fault, because her foolishness had caused the whole situation.

"He doesn't look pleased," observed Ben, hurrying her away.

"What's the rush?"

"Tony wants you urgently—Paula Krantz has set up an interview for American television."

"With my face like this?" Carrie protested. "Are you sure, Ben?"

"Positive."

Paula herself came forward to meet them. "No time to change, Carrie dear; straight into the studio."

Carrie was hurried into the Portakabin that housed the Independent Television sports team; it was full of people. She was thrust into a chair, a makeup girl whisked an overall around Carrie's shoulders and, nimble fingers flashing, spread thick pancake makeup over Carrie's whole face to minimize the redness and bruising, then whisked a comb through her hair.

"We're in luck," Paula said. "Hana Mandlikova was due to be interviewed, but her match is still on court, and they've booked satellite time. The questions'll be very straight—just about your contract with the circuit for next year, your hopes for the future, all that kind of stuff."

"Right," said Carrie, making an effort to be patient. Surely Paula must have the hide of a rhinoceros to arrange this when Carrie was patently exhausted and looking her very worst.

"Here she is," said Paula gushingly to the interviewer, a strikingly youthful, gray-haired, tanned man who might have been any age from thirty to fifty-five. "Caroline Astell, but her friends and her fans call her Carrie, and she'd like you to call her Carrie too. She had a little accident with the right side of her face, so if she could sit left side to camera I'd appreciate it."

"Hi," said the interviewer. "Call me David. I've

gone through the questions with Paula—you'll be okay."

He was more confident of that than Carrie was. She was used to interviews for British television, but it was usually with people she knew—and what was more, she didn't trust Paula. She settled herself in the black swivel chair, checked the cameras—the one opposite her was presumably the one to speak to—and looked around the studio. There was Paula, standing behind the cameras and smiling encouragingly, cameramen, a girl with headphones and a clipboard and a sound recordist fixing a microphone to Carrie's dress. "Say something for voice level, dear," said the recordist.

"One two three four five," said Carrie numbly. Her feet ached; her muscles were beginning to tighten. She badly needed to shower and change.

"Tell me about yourself," said the interviewer. "Do you enjoy tennis? We've a minute to go."

"I enjoy tennis very much, David," said Carrie.

"That's good to hear. Thirty seconds and all's well."

A television screen in the corner spluttered into life, and an earnestly talking woman appeared. They were now linked up to the American program, and David swung into his introduction, smiling and chatting with marvelous composure. "And we're very lucky indeed to have one of the brightest rising stars of world tennis with us here in Wimbledon. She's just come fresh from a singles and a mixed-doubles victory—how does it feel to win, Carrie?"

Sore, aching and in need of a bath, thought Carrie. She answered his conventional questions automatically and breathed a sigh of relief when the break for commercials interrupted them.

"Is that it?" she said hopefully.

"No; now we're joined by Nikolai Zanov," said the interviewer.

It was the last thing Carrie had expected. She caught Paula Krantz's eye; the older woman looked smug. She's planning something, thought Carrie, probably trying to revive the story of a romance between me and Nikolai.

As she was thinking, Zanov sat down beside her, still in his tennis clothes. I'm not going to let Paula get away with this, thought Carrie, and she stood up. "Please excuse me," she said politely. "I must have a shower and change." She left the Portakabin despite the protests of the interviewer and walked toward the changing room, head down, annoyed with Paula.

In a moment Nikolai was beside her. "Is anything wrong? Are you ill?"

"I thought Paula had set us up for some publicity stunt, and it was just too much—especially since I've sat around for her with my muscles stiffening long enough already."

Nikolai walked along beside her. "When you have showered, I will meet you and we'll have tea. There is no point now in trying to keep up any pretense, and I would like to be with you."

"But Alexei—"

"But Alexei will have to grin and bear it," said Nikolai flatly. "If he has anything to say to me, we can sort it out between us. Just so long as you stay away from him."

Carrie felt too much was being made of a comparatively minor incident. "He only asked me some questions," she said. "He didn't hit me or anything."

"No. He frightened you. He's a past master at

frightening people. Leave Alexei to me, and go and change."

Sitting, having tea with Nikolai, such an apparently everyday event, seemed extraordinary to Carrie after the hole-in-corner atmosphere of the last few weeks. Nikolai seemed less troubled, more wholeheartedly her companion than he had recently been; he smiled and chatted to various acquaintances, and Carrie was very conscious of all the curious and calculating glances the pair of them attracted from journalists and other players. Certainly Nikolai was making a most public declaration of their relationship; he never socialized with other players in the ordinary way, and tea with his doubles partner was an extraordinary event.

Ben sat watching them from a discreet distance.

"Is he guarding you?" asked Nikolai. "He has followed you since you came off court."

"I think he thinks I need looking after," said Carrie.

"And he also thinks I should do it," said Nikolai acutely. This was so close to what Ben had said that Carrie choked over her tea. "But as I can't look after you, he will," Nikolai went on. "That's not such a bad idea."

"You were annoyed with Ben before," said Carrie, not understanding his change of attitude.

"Only because he had opportunities that I lacked. But now we need no longer hide—now there is nothing to lose by being seen together—I don't envy him at all." He smiled, his teeth very white against the dark tan of his face.

"This is very English," he said, his gesture embracing the black-uniformed waitresses, the officials of the All-England Lawn Tennis Club in their white flannel trousers and blue blazers, and the quiet buzz of polite conversation from the other tables. "In this atmosphere my life seems preposterous. Sonya's situation seems unbelievable."

"Not to me," said Carrie. "I've been imagining what it must be like for you and for her. All the tea and the cakes in the world won't help me forget the danger she's in."

Nikolai took her hand in his much larger, muscular hand, and the physical contact made her catch her breath. "Not long now," he said. "If all goes well, she will be safely out of Russia soon."

9

～∞∞∞∞∞∞∞～

After tea Tony insisted that Carrie return to the hotel to rest. She agreed reluctantly. She was very tired, but she was reluctant to miss any opportunity of being with Nikolai. Ben joined them in the car, and for a while they sat in companionable silence.

"How was Paula?" Carrie asked eventually.

Tony shrugged. "Not pleased, but she'll get over it. Paula's an intelligent woman and alarmingly efficient, but she tends to leave people's feelings out of her calculations. If you don't want to talk about Nikolai Zanov, to me or to Paula or to the American public, in my view that's up to you, so forget the whole incident."

"Talking about incidents, Zanov and Alexei Peters had a fight right after you went to change, Carrie," said Ben.

"Did they?" This merely confirmed what Carrie already suspected. "Do you mean just an argument?"

163

"No, they came to blows. Alexei kept pushing Zanov and blocking his way, and finally Zanov hit him."

"Zanov's a big fellow, of course. Strong. One of the fastest servers in world tennis," said Tony reflectively.

"Alexei looked furious," said Ben.

Listening to this, Carrie had no doubt that soon Nikolai would be under even stricter guard, and so it proved. Next day Alexei had been joined by two large, silent men who looked very like the bodyguards she had seen with him in Rome. They arrived in the tournament car with Nikolai, waited for him outside the changing room and the court, and as soon as he was finished playing, whisked him back to the hotel. Sasha was nowhere to be seen most of the time; no loss, thought Carrie, though she no longer found thoughts of the other woman at all painful since Nikolai had explained the nature of their relationship.

Carrie refused even to think what would happen if Sonya didn't get away; in the long nights she lay awake tossing and turning, remembering the times, so cruelly short, she had spent with Nikolai.

He was playing skillful, inventive tennis; both their mixed-doubles matches had been easy victories, and he joked and laughed with Carrie, but he was preoccupied, and he seemed very tired to her. There had also been a change in the style of his play—he no longer produced powerhouse serves nor did he range round the court with his usual energy.

On Tuesday evening of the final week Ben was driving Carrie and Tony back to the hotel from a television studio. As they went through the park Carrie was at first content to rest, closing her eyes and letting the breeze lift her hair with its promise of cool after a blazing hot day. The two men were wrangling amiably about the advantages of a double-handed stroke for women, and Carrie broke in unceremoniously. "Have either of you noticed the change in Nikolai's play?"

"Yes, of course," said Tony, surprised that she should even ask. "Isn't he injured?"

"That's the first I've heard of it." He can't be so injured he has to withdraw, thought Carrie. It would be too cruel, just as he's so close to freedom. "Who told you that?"

"Nobody. It's what everybody's saying because he's playing defensive tennis and running as little as possible; though I must say, I've watched him closely, and I can't work out for the life of me where the injury is—you can usually tell from the way a man moves, but not in his case."

"He hasn't said anything to me. Could he just be tired?"

"More than tired, exhausted," said Tony thoughtfully. "That would explain his tactics—trying to conserve energy—but I don't see why he should be. He's always shown outstanding stamina—it's one of his greatest assets—and this tournament has been perfectly normal so far. The weather's been good, and there have been so few postponed and interrupted matches that it must have been one of the least stressful Wimbledon championships for years, at least five years."

"But Nikolai's still tired."

"Perhaps he's worried about something?" suggested Tony tactfully. Carrie fully appreciated the self-control which made him refrain from discussing her relationship with Nikolai; he also refrained from commenting on Ben's continued presence at her side.

"I'm sure it's not an injury," Ben put in. "I saw him

doing warm-up exercises this morning, and he was perfectly sound."

"If Zanov doesn't run more, Lendl will have an easy win in the semifinal," said Tony.

But by then it'll be Thursday, and it won't matter, thought Carrie; Sonya will be safe, and if Nikolai loses the match, it won't make any difference. She dragged her attention back to Tony, who was pursuing his own line of thought. "Mind you, if Zanov doesn't take too much out of himself in the singles, then he'll be fitter for your doubles semifinal. I'd enjoy watching you play the final in that, Carrie—you make a beautiful team."

Carrie laughed. "That's a romantic observation for you."

"Not to look at," said Tony with infinite scorn, "though I suppose he's a good-looking enough chap, and you take after your mother, of course. No, I meant as tennis players."

"Realistically, we don't have a chance," said Carrie. "Not playing the number-one seeds in the semifinal just an hour after Nikolai's singles match ends."

"You were unlucky with the schedules," admitted Tony, "but you know my views on assuming you'll lose. No match is over until the umpire calls game, set and match."

Next day was Carrie's singles semifinal. She was packing her clothes in the morning when she heard a knock on the door and Paula's voice calling, "May I come in?" Before Carrie had a chance to answer, the door opened and Paula burst into the room, a startling sight in mauve chiffon, a huge picture hat and diamonds, and engulfed her in a scented embrace.

"You look magnificent," said Carrie.

"Why, thank you, dear, I'm going to meet royalty this afternoon, and I don't want to let them down. I'm just thrilled about it, but that's not what I'm here to speak to you about. I want a word in your ear about this afternoon."

"What about it?"

"The dress you choose—make it extra-feminine. I want you to look a real womanly woman; it'll please the sponsors, and the television coverage of this match is going to the U.S. via satellite. It's a real pity you're playing Chrissie Lloyd."

"Why?" Carrie was bemused.

"Two blondes, that's why. So much more dramatic if it's one blonde, one brunette. Never mind; can't be helped. Will you wear your hair loose?"

"I don't want to play a match with loose hair, it gets in the way. If you want me to stand a chance, you'll just have to put up with it," said Carrie firmly, but Paula dismissed that.

"Come on, dear, we both know that your chances of beating Chrissie at this point in time are about as good as my chances of marrying Prince Charles. Your games are too similar. Now next year, when you've a little more tactical experience and more confidence, I wouldn't be surprised, but for the moment you could leave your hair loose as a favor to old Paula."

"Certainly not," said Carrie, amused both by Paula's obstinacy and her shrewdness. She was quite right about the likely outcome of the match.

By three thirty on Wednesday afternoon the center court umpire was calling "Game, set and match to Mrs. Lloyd; six-four, five-seven, seven-five," and an exhausted Carrie was shaking hands with her opponent and thanking the umpire. She had never played so well, and it had been a close match. Next year I'll do it, she thought, collecting her rackets; Paula was right. The applause from the capacity crowd went on and on; Carrie scanned the players' seats looking for Nikolai. He was standing at the back, and when he saw her looking, he stretched his hands toward her and applauded her directly. Then Karel Vronsky spoke to him, and he suddenly slipped away. With his departure Carrie's euphoria left her, and she joined Mrs. Lloyd for the curtsey to the royal box in a storm of applause she didn't hear.

She stood in the shower, too tired to think, happy to let the water wash away the stiffness from her muscles and the tension from her neck. She was content with the afternoon's result. She had played well; she couldn't have done more. The crowd had had their money's worth, and presumably the American cosmetic company would feel they had hired a reasonable tennis-player, even if she did tie her hair back. Carrie smiled a little at the thought of Paula and turned up the heat of the shower.

"Get a move on; you're clean by now," said a voice, familiar but indistinct through the noise of the shower.

"Betty? Is that you?" said Carrie, stretching for a towel. Her mother enveloped her in a large towel and began rubbing her back vigorously. "Come on, girl, get those muscles loosened up."

Carrie was delighted at this unexpected arrival. "Why didn't you tell me you were coming? Did you see the match?"

"I only decided at the last moment, and yes, I did see the match. You remembered to curtsey to the royal box. Well done." Betty Astell's eyes were full of pride, but she was always undemonstrative, and Carrie knew that was all the praise she'd get. It was quite enough.

They joined Tony, Ben and Paula for a celebration tea that was constantly interrupted by other players, officials and members of the All-England Club with congratulations.

"It's as if I'd won," said Carrie finally, overwhelmed.

"A defeat like that is a victory," said Paula. "I watched from a television control room, and there was a very positive response there. You behaved so well; I was real proud of you all through that match—you didn't argue a single line call, though in my opinion one of the baseline judges needs either glasses or brain surgery. And not only didn't you argue the calls, you even smiled and congratulated Chrissie as if you meant it. Camera two had good footage of that smile."

"Carrie never argues on court," said Tony, shocked. "It's bad sportsmanship, and it breaks concentration." Carrie smiled at her mother—they'd both heard this so often it was a family joke. But Paula swept on, oblivious.

"Now we've got the mixed-doubles semifinal to look forward to, and maybe even the final. I don't know how Zanov will take the news, of course."

For Carrie the world stopped. All color drained from her face, and for a moment she thought she would faint. "What news?" she forced herself to ask.

"About his sister, Sonya," said Paula. "The one who was under house arrest in Moscow last week—it was in all the papers, don't you remember?"

"Yes."

"Well, a news agency report has just come through

from Moscow. She tried to escape apparently, but they've recaptured her and she's in prison."

"Are you sure?"

"I'm sure that's what the bulletin from Tass said; it mightn't be true, though, the Russians often use that agency for whatever story they want the West to believe."

For the rest of that day Carrie clung to the belief that the news agency report was false. In a television interview she answered mechanically, unable to concentrate, and she couldn't eat dinner despite Tony's pressure.

Eventually her mother intervened. "Go to bed, Carrie. You can eat at breakfast." Carrie gave her mother a grateful look and escaped to her room, but not to sleep.

It was a long night. At three in the morning Ben appeared. "You didn't turn the light out; I've been keeping an eye on it. Are you all right?"

"More or less." He nodded disbelievingly and sat down in the sagging hotel armchair. "Do go to bed, Ben. You look shattered."

"I can't sleep. I think I'm in love."

"Really? Who with?"

"Dallas, but I'm more interested in you just now. Are you worrying about Zanov?" She nodded. "Tell you what, how about a game of three-card stud?" So she spent the next two hours playing poker until, just as the first hint of dawn crept into the sky, she fell asleep.

"You look terrible," said Tony bluntly at breakfast. "No practice this morning—go back to bed."

"No, thank you."

"Come shopping with me," said Betty. "Take your mind off tennis altogether." That idea was much more appealing to Carrie; she persuaded Ben to relax his watch, and she and Betty had a leisurely London morning of shops and chat. Despite herself, Carrie found she was being distracted from her worry; Betty was good company and she noticed the time with surprise. "Nikolai's match is at two," she said. "Let's grab a taxi, or we'll be late."

"I didn't know you wanted to see this match," said Betty as they settled back in the seats. "Zanov's not likely to win, is he? Tony tells me he's tired or ill."

"Don't say he won't win," Carrie begged.

"Why not?"

Carrie shrugged. "I can't explain. If Sonya really is in prison, then the match doesn't matter anyway."

"Rain will probably stop play," said Betty. "Look at the sky." And indeed for the first time that week the radiant blue of the summer sky was obscured by threatening dark clouds.

As the taxi crawled along, maddeningly slow in the traffic, Carrie was saying to herself, Let it rain, let it rain. Please let it rain. If Nikolai's match could be delayed long enough, then the mixed doubles couldn't take place that day—more precious hours would have been gained for Sonya's journey. If indeed the Russian woman wasn't sitting in a jail.

They reached Wimbledon at two thirty; the match was already in progress. Tony was keeping seats for them at the back, and as Carrie sat down he whispered, "Something odd's going on. Zanov's up to something; he keeps arguing with the umpire."

Even now the match was halted while Nikolai disputed a line call. "Play on," said the umpire, and Zanov very slowly returned to the baseline and prepared to serve. The scoreboard told the state of the match so far; Nikolai was down at two games to three, but as he was serving, that meant that no one had yet broken serve and the game was still even. Unusually for him, Zanov bounced the ball several times before serving. He looked utterly weary.

The match ground on; Nikolai used every device possible to slow it down. He queried line calls, delayed his own services, declared he wasn't ready for his opponent's serves, lingered at the umpire's chair at end-changes. The crowd, at first enthusiastic, was becoming hostile. Although Zanov had a reputation as an extrovert and a clown, he was not usually a bad sportsman, but today he was using all the well-worn tactics of gamesmanship, and the crowd didn't like it. The more outrageous his behavior became, the louder the cries of disapproval; and Zanov exploited that, too, appealing to the umpire to control the crowd and waiting while they quieted down. Lendl took all this with imperturbable composure, waiting patiently, concentrating on the game.

Meanwhile the sky was darkening and clouding over. It must rain, thought Carrie, her heart wrenching with sympathy for Nikolai. How terrible it was for him, she thought, playing tennis with his whole future at stake—the pressure would be too much.

"Carrie," whispered Karel Vronsky in her ear, "I want to talk to you." She followed him outside, down the corridor, into a tiny storeroom in the heart of the center court stands. Above her she could hear the shuffling of feet almost drowning the umpire's voice as the match proceeded on its even course. The fat man propped himself against a sink and sighed. He looked despairing; his jowls hung in lugubrious folds, and he was sweating profusely. "I have a message from Nikolai Theodorovich. He has heard information from friends in Moscow—a friend he relies on. It is not true that Sonya is in prison. So far the authorities haven't found her."

"But still there is no news of her arrival in the West?" said Carrie, irrationally hopeful. The Russian gestured behind him, toward the court. "Would he be playing for time like this if she was safe?"

"Karel, what's the matter with him? Is he ill?"

"He is not allowed to sleep," said Vronsky. "Alexei and Sasha between them will not let him sleep. They keep watch." His voice was filled with contempt and resentment.

"That's ridiculous! Isn't he meant to play well for Russia? Why would they damage his chances like that?"

"Alexei is not doing this for the government," said Karel. "He is doing it for revenge, because they fought some days ago and Nikolai Theodorovich won. Alexei cannot damage him openly—his masters would not like that. But lack of sleep is difficult to prove. Alexei will get away with it, and Nikolai Theodorovich will have played his last game in the West. Listen to it." He jerked a thumb at the court; the hostile shouts of the crowd echoed in the tiny room.

"This isn't the last match. We have the mixed doubles to play."

Vronsky shrugged. "You think he will be fit to play again after only an hour's rest? Fit enough to help you defeat Aron and Copley? I'm sorry, but I don't think so."

"Why didn't he go into one of the massage rooms reserved for players and sleep there? Alexei couldn't have disturbed him, and he'd certainly have improved enough to stand a chance; in any case we're more likely to win the doubles than he is to defeat Lendl. They've played seven times this season, and Nikolai only won three—and that was at peak fitness. Didn't you suggest withdrawing from the singles to him?"

The Russian shrugged again. "Of course I did. He wouldn't listen. It was not fair to you, he said. Too much to ask. And if the match was lost and he had to go back to Russia, he said it would be a bad memory for you."

"It would indeed," said Carrie, chilled. The full weight of her responsibility was beginning to dawn on her. "What will happen to Nikolai if he has to go back to Russia?"

"There are some questions better not answered," said Vronsky, avoiding her eyes.

"I want to know the answer," she pressed.

"He doesn't want you to know," said Vronsky. "He was very insistent."

There was a moment of quiet, then another hostile roar from the crowd. The Russian shook his head bitterly—there were tears in his eyes. "Not like this," he said. "They should not remember him like this. In all my years of coaching, never, never have I known such a talent. But whatever the talent, whatever the courage, he cannot play without rest. I *told* him: You have a better chance in the mixed doubles. It is all so stupid. It is good for no one. I am finished with it. No more coaching. No more work for the Party or for Russian tennis. If Nikolai goes back, then I go with him. But otherwise I stay here."

A grumbling murmur and scattered applause from the crowd greeted the umpire's announcement that Nikolai had won the first set. "That'll be the last he wins as well," said Vronsky grimly. "Lendl's much too good a player to mess around with."

And so it proved. Carrie watched with growing misery as the cool player powered his way to victory against an opponent who was obviously finding it almost impossible to concentrate. Toward the end of the fourth set with the score five-two to Lendl, the crowd suddenly switched allegiance. In some mysterious way the spectators seemed to realize that Zanov, whose delaying tactics had grown more and more halfhearted, was drawing on reserves of pure courage to continue playing at all; they cheered his every effort. Slowly, point by painful point, he clawed his way back to five games all.

It was four, and still it did not rain, though the cloud cover made the light very bad, and Carrie could feel the humidity on her cheek. Thunder rumbled in the far distance, mixing imperceptibly with the drone of a jet on the flight path to Heathrow. "Za-nov, Za-nov" chanted a little group of teenage girls.

Zanov was serving; he waited, head bowed, while the umpire quieted his fans. Then he double-faulted. "Love-fifteen," said the umpire. He moved along the baseline to serve to the other court, and double-faulted again. "Love-thirty." Carrie buried her head in her hands. The next point Zanov served well, but Lendl smashed an untouchable return. "Love-forty." Another double-fault. "Game to Lendl. Lendl leads by six games to five. . . ."

The last game passed in a flash. Lendl served three aces, won a valiant rally, and was through to the final. Carrie felt sick. She saw Vronsky hurry onto the court and talk to Nikolai. They were arguing; Nikolai was shaking his head in refusal. She ran down through the corridors to meet them, pushing her way through reporters and fans. Zanov and Vronsky were still arguing in Russian; Alexei, behind them, looked pleased.

"Nikolai . . ." Carrie began. He noticed her with a

smile of delight. In a swift movement he unceremoniously dumped his rackets into Vronsky's arms and
hugged her. Flashbulbs popped, and she could hear a
commotion as Vronsky held Alexei away from them,
but she closed her eyes and leaned against Nikolai's
chest, oblivious. She could feel his heart beating, and
he murmured, "Carrie, Carrie," brushing her face
with little kisses. There was a fresh outbreak of
flashbulbs, and a worried official tried to move them
along. "Excuse me, er—you're causing an obstruc-
tion. I'm so sorry."

Vronsky burst into Russian and pushed Alexei's face
into the wall. "Good heavens," said the official, a
portly man who would never see seventy again. "I
don't think, er—"

"So *that's* where you've got to," said Ben's voice.
"I'm just in time to join the fun, I see." Politely he
moved Vronsky to one side and took Alexei's arm in a
firm grip. "You and I have a lot to talk about, Peters,"
he said. Behind them Carrie could just see the bodyguards, immovably jammed in a crowd. "We'll leave
you to it, Ben," she said.

"My pleasure."

Zanov led the way to an untenanted office with
Vronsky bringing up the rear. The door shut and
comparative peace restored, Vronsky turned to Carrie. "You must talk to Nikolai. Tell him he is mad. Stop
him."

Zanov put his arm around Carrie and hugged her
again. "I'm sorry," he said. "I cannot play our match
this afternoon—I must withdraw."

"What?" demanded Carrie.

"You see, he is quite mad," said Vronsky, and
Nikolai snapped at him in Russian.

Carrie faced them both. "Nikolai, you have just

under an hour to sleep. Please . . . think about it after you've rested. I couldn't bear it if you didn't play just because of me. If you're too exhausted or too ill, that's another matter, but if you want to spare me the strain, surely that should be my decision?"

He shook his head wearily. "You don't understand."

"Explain."

"I want to keep you free of all the mess and suffering—I don't want you to be involved."

"But I am," said Carrie. "You have one chance—take it. We can win."

"Against Aron and Copley?"

"Everyone keeps saying 'Aron and Copley' as if they were magic. They're just two tennis players, like us, but individually they're not as good as we are."

"Not when I'm fit."

"Go and rest. We'll talk about it later."

He shook his head again, but this time in resignation. "You are quite decided?"

"Completely."

"Thank you."

"Thank me when we win," said Carrie with far more confidence than she felt, and leaving Nikolai in Vronsky's care, she went in search of Ben and Tony.

"Carrie! Thank heavens!" Tony looked worried. "Is it true that Zanov's retired from the match?"

"No."

"How is he?"

"Resting." They were standing in the bar, surrounded by curious stares and eager listeners. "Let's go somewhere quiet . . . and I'd like Betty to hear what I have to say."

Fifteen minutes later Carrie finished her account of the situation. Betty flashed her a sympathetic glance and said nothing. Tony cleared his throat. "Just to make sure I've got this straight. Zanov has gone virtually without sleep for the past five days. He has just come off court after nearly three hours of punishing tennis. Shortly you are to play a match which, if he loses, will mean that he has to return permanently to Russia to face God knows what. Am I right?"

Carrie nodded.

"And this is very important to you because you're in love with him."

Carrie nodded again.

"Right," said Tony briskly. "We'd better work on tactics. Let's assume you're playing this match virtually single-handed. Put Zanov at the net and you take the baseline. You take the right-hand court; you take the first serve. And play attacking tennis. Every shot you can't angle past the opposition, you hit at their feet, hard enough to be unreturnable. No rallies, just killers, every time."

"Remember Janet Copley has a weak forehand. Nothing to her backhand if you can help it," said Betty.

"And you'd better eat some chocolate. Now. Your blood sugar level needs to be at an all-time high when you step on court."

It'll take more than chocolate to win this match, thought Carrie as she sat in the waiting room opposite Keith Aron, a burly Canadian, and the Australian Janet Copley, deceptively slim and fragile-looking. They were chatting and laughing, obviously confident; of course they were, they'd seen Zanov's match with Lendl. The waiting room was unpleasantly humid, and Carrie could still hear rumbles of thunder, but there was still no sign of rain. The clock on the wall said just after six; Carrie watched the door anxiously. Tony patted her knee reassuringly. "That clock's always fast."

The door opened. Karel Vronsky entered followed by a livelier-looking Zanov. After a hurried discussion of tactics Vronsky agreed with Tony's plans for the match.

"Too much work for Carrie," objected Nikolai, but Carrie brushed his objection aside.

"I'm looking forward to it," she said, and it was almost true. Now the match was imminent she looked forward to doing something positive rather than just sitting on the sidelines as a spectator. As they walked on to the court she was very conscious of Nikolai close beside her. His hair was still damp from the shower, and there was an alertness to his step—even the short rest had helped. The sky was still thunderous and overcast, but perversely, Carrie now dreaded the rain; she was keyed up to playing, and she wanted to get the match over with.

Play lasted an hour and a quarter, and for most of that time victory hung in the balance. It seemed an eternity for Carrie, an eternity where every shot counted and every mistake was a disaster, where she was running too slowly, serving too feebly, never doing enough.

They won the first set six-four, but in the second Carrie began to tire. As they changed ends at two-five down, Carrie felt crushed. She didn't dare look toward the players' seats; she was sure Alexei would be there, crowing. She sipped water from a paper cup, chewed a glucose tablet and tried not to cry. Nikolai joined her. "Now I shall take over," he said. "You have done enough. From now on you stay at the net, and don't go for every ball. Rely on me. Let them take this game with Keith's serve—the set's gone already. But next set we will win. Trust me." Carrie shook her head, still near to tears; he gripped her shoulders and gave her a little encouraging squeeze. "You have played superbly—better than anyone could expect. You've played a singles game in a doubles match. Now it is time for me to do my share."

And for the last set he did more than his share; he played with a mastery and a strength to which his opponents could find no answer. The crowd, quiet during the early part of the match in sympathy with Carrie's lone struggle, were relieved to have something to applaud, and they did. "Za-nov! Za-nov!" chanted his frenzied fans.

"Quiet, please," appealed the umpire in vain as the third set progressed. "Mr. Zanov and Miss Astell lead three games to one."

Keith Aron served three aces and the next game was lost, but after that it was straightforward. Carrie had now rested enough to help, and the last three games were short and businesslike.

"Game, set and match to Mr. Zanov and Miss Astell . . ." the umpire began, and his words were drowned by applause. Carrie ran to the net, clasped hands with her opponents, thanked the umpire and smiled at the crowd in a happy daze. Nikolai caught her hand and turned her to face him. For a moment they stared into each other's eyes, too relieved to speak. "Two more days," he said. "You have given me two more days. . . ." Before he could finish, they were surrounded by well-wishers and Carrie was engulfed by photographers. When she looked around, Nikolai had gone.

And after all, she reflected next morning in the gray

light of a rainy day, unless Sonya arrived before Saturday afternoon, the situation was still as bad as it had ever been. Not even the congratulations and the enthusiasm that had followed their success could change the grim facts of Nikolai's situation.

Carrie stayed at the hotel all day, hoping for news, but no news came. Jimmy did his best to cheer her up, unsuccessfully; Tony was out all day at Wimbledon and Ben, pleased with himself at having had the opportunity to push Alexei around, watched tennis on the hotel television all afternoon. Carrie couldn't bear to watch or to listen; the familiar sounds of a tennis game brought back to her the previous day's anxiety. She went to bed early and slept dreamlessly.

The telephone woke her at six o'clock. It was Nikolai. Her heart jumped, expecting news of Sonya's arrival.

"I'm at Alice's flat. Could you meet me there in half an hour?" She could tell from his tone there was no good news yet.

Agreeing to meet him, Carrie replaced the receiver and hurried to shower, then hesitated over the choice of clothes. Something in Nikolai's voice warned her that he might be seeing her only to say good-bye; deliberately she pushed this thought from her mind, refusing to pick special 'last meeting' clothes. She would wear jeans and a casual velour top. Still, she brushed her hair till it shone, and her face was alight with happiness at the prospect of seeing Nikolai.

She walked through the still-deserted streets. An occasional dustcart rumbled by, a milkman carried crates into a hotel, but they were only reminders that London was alive. Overhead the sky, pale blue and cloudless, promised a perfect day for the men's final—

and, she remembered with a shock, the mixed-doubles final that she was to play in. A final on the center court. A month ago that thought would have loomed large in the forefront of her mind, but now it was just another match. Reality lay with Nikolai; every step taking her closer to their meeting was important, nothing else seemed to matter.

He was standing waiting for her outside the block of flats, leaning against one of the great stone pillars that flanked the majestic flight of steps leading up to the Albert Hall. He was looking in the other direction, his attention caught by a flock of pigeons squabbling over food. He was dressed casually, in jeans and a cream suede shirt, and his whole body gave an impression of compelling, relaxed power. Then he saw her, and in seconds they clung together; Carrie hugged him, burying her head in his chest, feeling utterly safe, her body molded to his.

"We haven't much time," he said. "Soon Alexei will come." He took her hand and they walked up the steps, toward Hyde Park. Carrie's throat was choked; she felt too much to speak. Besides, there was so much, and so little, to say.

"No word from Sonya?" she said tentatively.

He shook his head. "That is why we must talk. Tonight, after the match, I will return to Russia." He hesitated. Carrie thought, *I will remember this forever —the feeling of the springy grass under my feet, the radiant early morning light touching the surface of the lake and burnishing it silver, the cool strength of Nikolai's hand on mine.* Behind them a solitary rider cantered down Rotten Row, the sand spurting up from the horse's hoofs; time seemed to stop, and they shared a moment of pure joy.

"I love you, Carrie," said Nikolai. "I love you more than I have ever loved anyone, more than I thought it was possible to love." She began to speak, but he went on. "In a situation like mine, talk of love is selfish. Tonight I go back to Russia, and I will never return to the West."

"You don't know that."

"Yes, I do." His certainty silenced her, and she attempted no more argument. "If things were different, I could have shown you my love. I could have kept you safe, made you happy—I like to think that. All I have caused you is grief."

"I love you, Nikolai," said Carrie quietly. "That can't be just grief. The last weeks have been the happiest in my life."

"And the saddest?" He was looking at her perceptively, and she had to agree.

"Yes—the saddest too. But I wouldn't change a moment of it." They had wandered over to the banks of the Serpentine, deserted at this early hour.

Nikolai pulled Carrie to him and held her close. "I love you," he said again. "I desire you. I want to be with you forever."

"I'll come with you to Russia," said Carrie. "Please." She was so moved, she could hardly speak. "Please, Nikolai. I belong with you."

"I must go," he said, and gently turned her.

She saw Alexei and two burly men advancing toward them across the grass, incongruous in their dark suits and raincoats in the glory of the early morning park. Fifty yards away Nikolai joined them; the bodyguards, one each side of him, looked clumsy and brutish against the supple strength of his athlete's body. Alexei smiled at Carrie, a triumphant, gloating smile, and waved mockingly. Nikolai walked away without looking back, head bent; after a moment's hesitation Alexei followed him, and Carrie was alone.

Everyone told Carrie that the men's singles final was one of the classics. She didn't watch it. Avoiding company, she sat on a bench in the general changing room. Soon she would join Tracy Austin in the special dressing room of the center court, but she wanted to be alone as long as possible. She stared at the hands of her watch as they ticked round the dial. When the men finished, the mixed doubles was on. She dreaded going out on court with Nikolai, knowing it was the last time she would see him. Her mind whirled with wild impulses—she'd follow him to Russia; she'd urge him to stay in the West and let Sonya look after herself; but she knew that either was impossible. They'd said good-bye that morning—it was his decision. She'd never felt so miserable, so utterly wretched, in her life before. Withdrawing from the match was impossible; Tony, Betty, Paula, the tournament organizers, the press, the public—she couldn't let them down, and she wouldn't. At last a final massive roar warned her that the singles was over; she picked up her racket bag and stepped into the corridor.

Ben was sitting just outside the door.

"What are you doing here? I told you I'd be safe. You've missed the men's final! Ben, you shouldn't have!"

"I can always watch it on video," he said stubbornly. "I haven't forgiven you for giving me the slip this morning."

"But video's never the same. You miss the atmosphere. You've sat in this corridor for over two hours."

"Plenty more men's finals; only one Carrie Astell. Stop fussing!"

Betty had told her about the treatment given to finalists; the bouquets sent along to the dressing room, the solicitous attention paid by the officials, the formal escort from the dressing-room door down to the little waiting room behind the center court. At any other time she would have enjoyed it, but now it was flat, and she gazed at the pictures on the waiting-room walls with sightless eyes. At first she and Tracy were alone with the officials; then, in a flurry of concern, another set of officials entered with John Austin but without Nikolai.

The officials were nearing dignified panic when at last he appeared; their standard briefing to the players on Royal etiquette—bowing or curtseying before the match, what to do when receiving trophies after it—was noticeably brisker than usual, and the players were hurried onto the court.

"Why were you late?" asked Carrie, making an effort to be casual.

"I waited for a phone call. Pavel was supposed to ring me this morning."

So there was still no news. Carrie had almost, but not quite, stopped hoping. She looked at the competitors' box; Tony looking anxious, Betty smiling, Ben, of course, Sasha tapping her nails impatiently, Jimmy talking earnestly to her; behind them, looking pleased with himself, Alexei. Then a clutch of Americans, evidently family and friends of the Austins; and beside them an elegant middle-aged man, half-familiar . . . Then Carrie realized.

"Nikolai, look, Bunin's over there."

Bunin was gesturing with his hands—the thumbs-up sign. Then Karel Vronsky appeared in the competitors' box, and there was no mistaking his message. He was waving with great exultant sweeps of his bearlike arms, craggy face alight with triumph. Nikolai ran over to speak to his coach, climbing through ranks of spectators; a buzz of interest ran through the spectators as they sensed something out of the ordinary happening. In a few moments he was back at Carrie's side. "It's true! Sonya's arrived in England!" He enveloped her in a crushing embrace.

"Not now, Nikolai," protested Carrie. "The umpire's calling us." She was laughing with relief and clinging to him.

"Will you marry me?"

"We have to play the match."

"Make love to me, then."

"On the center court?"

"I will if you will." He picked her up bodily in his arms and carried her over to the umpire's chair. She had never seen him so happy.

"Come on, Miss Astell," he said, putting her down. "Enough of this time wasting. Get your racket and we'll play."

Bemused with the suddenness of events and swamped with relief, Carrie picked up a racket, but Nikolai removed it from her grip. "Wet-weather stringing," he chided gently. "Now I know you love me; you're confused enough to take the wrong racket. Very unprofessional."

It was a joy to see the change in Nikolai. Once more the entertainer, his body moving lithely and freely round the court, he played supremely well; joking with Carrie, with the ball boys, with the crowd, never interfering with his opponents' concentration but preserving at the same time the lighthearted skill that distinguishes mixed-doubles matches, he deserved to win. But Carrie's concentration was gone; she was swamped, buoyed up with happiness. Her tennis crumbled, and it was a quick victory for the Austins.

It was a wonder to the photographers who clustered round after the game ended that the defeated pair looked, if anything, happier than the winners.

As they walked out of the court through the passageway leading up to the royal box they were momentarily free of the pressmen who concentrated on the Austins' trophy award. Nikolai and Carrie waited to step back into the crowd's view once more to collect their runner-up prizes.

"Now," said Nikolai, "we can have a courtship. With dinners and presents. Then we can have a proposal of marriage. Then you can accept my proposal, and we'll live—"

"That's a point," said Carrie. "What'll you live on? If you give up tennis?"

"Violin concerts. And my Swiss bank account."

"Do you really have one?" Carrie couldn't tell if he was serious.

"I've been playing tennis for ten years now. Not all my winnings went to the Party. Carrie, come here." Three escorting officials looked away with British courtesy and reserve as he kissed her thoroughly. At last one of them tapped him on the shoulder.

"Er—sorry and all that, but you must collect your trophy now." Nikolai looked at him, one eyebrow raised mockingly. "This is my trophy," he said, indicating Carrie.

"And it's a trophy you'll have to collect later," she said teasingly.

"You can be sure I will. And then I have matters to settle with Alexei."

They stepped into the royal box, and Carrie looked down at the applauding crowd. Her parents were cheering unashamedly—Tony never cheers, she thought—but Alexei and Sasha had gone.

She bobbed her curtsey to royalty and murmured her thanks. "Zanov! Za-nov!" chanted the coterie of female fans. As they retreated down the steps into the passageway once more, Carrie could feel Nikolai's strong arms holding her. "Never let me go," she said.

"Never," he said, and pulled her close. "Never," he said again, and then his words were lost in kisses.

Genuine Silhouette
sterling silver bookmark
for only $15.95!

What a beautiful way to hold your place in your current romance! This genuine sterling silver bookmark, with the distinctive Silhouette symbol in elegant black, measures 1½" long and 1" wide. It makes a beautiful gift for yourself, and for every romantic you know! And, at only $15.95 each, including all postage and handling charges, you'll want to order several now, while supplies last.

Send your name and address with check or money order for $15.95 per bookmark ordered to
Simon & Schuster Enterprises
120 Brighton Rd., P.O. Box 5020
Clifton, N.J. 07012
Attn: Bookmark

Bookmarks can be ordered pre-paid only. No charges will be accepted. Please allow 4-6 weeks for delivery.

N.Y. State Residents
Please Add Sales Tax

YOU'LL BE SWEPT AWAY WITH SILHOUETTE DESIRE

$1.75 each

1 ☐ James	5 ☐ Baker	8 ☐ Dee
2 ☐ Monet	6 ☐ Mallory	9 ☐ Simms
3 ☐ Clay	7 ☐ St. Claire	10 ☐ Smith
4 ☐ Carey		

$1.95 each

11 ☐ James	29 ☐ Michelle	47 ☐ Michelle	65 ☐ Allison
12 ☐ Palmer	30 ☐ Lind	48 ☐ Powers	66 ☐ Langtry
13 ☐ Wallace	31 ☐ James	49 ☐ James	67 ☐ James
14 ☐ Valley	32 ☐ Clay	50 ☐ Palmer	68 ☐ Browning
15 ☐ Vernon	33 ☐ Powers	51 ☐ Lind	69 ☐ Carey
16 ☐ Major	34 ☐ Milan	52 ☐ Morgan	70 ☐ Victor
17 ☐ Simms	35 ☐ Major	53 ☐ Joyce	71 ☐ Joyce
18 ☐ Ross	36 ☐ Summers	54 ☐ Fulford	72 ☐ Hart
19 ☐ James	37 ☐ James	55 ☐ James	73 ☐ St. Clair
20 ☐ Allison	38 ☐ Douglass	56 ☐ Douglass	74 ☐ Douglass
21 ☐ Baker	39 ☐ Monet	57 ☐ Michelle	75 ☐ McKenna
22 ☐ Durant	40 ☐ Mallory	58 ☐ Mallory	76 ☐ Michelle
23 ☐ Sunshine	41 ☐ St. Claire	59 ☐ Powers	77 ☐ Lowell
24 ☐ Baxter	42 ☐ Stewart	60 ☐ Dennis	78 ☐ Barber
25 ☐ James	43 ☐ Simms	61 ☐ Simms	79 ☐ Simms
26 ☐ Palmer	44 ☐ West	62 ☐ Monet	80 ☐ Palmer
27 ☐ Conrad	45 ☐ Clay	63 ☐ Dee	81 ☐ Kennedy
28 ☐ Lovan	46 ☐ Chance	64 ☐ Milan	82 ☐ Clay

YOU'LL BE SWEPT AWAY WITH SILHOUETTE DESIRE
$1.95 each

83 ☐ Chance	100 ☐ Howard	117 ☐ Powers	134 ☐ McKenna
84 ☐ Powers	101 ☐ Morgan	118 ☐ Milan	135 ☐ Charlton
85 ☐ James	102 ☐ Palmer	119 ☐ John	136 ☐ Martel
86 ☐ Malek	103 ☐ James	120 ☐ Clay	137 ☐ Ross
87 ☐ Michelle	104 ☐ Chase	121 ☐ Browning	138 ☐ Chase
88 ☐ Trevor	105 ☐ Blair	122 ☐ Trent	139 ☐ St. Claire
89 ☐ Ross	106 ☐ Michelle	123 ☐ Paige	140 ☐ Joyce
90 ☐ Roszel	107 ☐ Chance	124 ☐ St. George	141 ☐ Morgan
91 ☐ Browning	108 ☐ Gladstone	125 ☐ Caimi	142 ☐ Nicole
92 ☐ Carey	109 ☐ Simms	126 ☐ Carey	143 ☐ Allison
93 ☐ Berk	110 ☐ Palmer	127 ☐ James	144 ☐ Evans
94 ☐ Robbins	111 ☐ Browning	128 ☐ Michelle	145 ☐ James
95 ☐ Summers	112 ☐ Nicole	129 ☐ Bishop	146 ☐ Knight
96 ☐ Milan	113 ☐ Cresswell	130 ☐ Blair	147 ☐ Scott
97 ☐ James	114 ☐ Ross	131 ☐ Larson	148 ☐ Powers
98 ☐ Joyce	115 ☐ James	132 ☐ McCoy	149 ☐ Galt
99 ☐ Major	116 ☐ Joyce	133 ☐ Monet	150 ☐ Simms

SILHOUETTE DESIRE, Department SD/6
1230 Avenue of the Americas
New York, NY 10020

Please send me the books I have checked above. I am enclosing $_____
(please add 75¢ to cover postage and handling. NYS and NYC residents please
add appropriate sales tax). Send check or money order—no cash or C.O.D.'s
please. Allow six weeks for delivery.

NAME_____

ADDRESS_____

CITY_____ STATE/ZIP_____